Plays on the Word

Plays on the Word

*Christian drama for churches,
schools and youth groups*

DEREK HAYLOCK

National Society/Church House Publishing
Church House, Great Smith Street, London SW1P 3NZ

National Society/Church House Publishing
Church House, Great Smith Street,
London SW1P 3NZ

ISBN 0 7151 4824 9

First Published in 1993 by The National Society and Church House Publishing

Performing Rights

Photocopying

Text design and typesetting by The National Society
Cover design by Leigh Hurlock
Printed in England by Streetsprinters, Baldock, Herts SG7 6NW

CONTENTS

* Reprinted from *Drama for Disciples*, National Society/Church House Publishing, 1988.

** Reprinted from *Acts for Apostles*, Church House Publishing, 1987.

N.B. The material in this book is arranged so that the pieces more suited for performance by children come at the beginning, and those more appropriate for performance by older teenagers or adults towards the end.

Preface

This collection of dramatic sketches is provided as a resource for all those wishing to explore a variety of ways of using drama to present and to experience the teaching of the Bible. Much of the material, particularly that in the first half of the book, is provided for use with fairly large groups of children, whereas other items in the second half of the book have been written with performance by adults or older teenagers in mind. The book is a successor to *Acts for Apostles*, *Drama for Disciples* and *Sketches from Scripture* (National Society/CHP). The reader will note that I have exhausted my stock of alliterative titles for these collections. However, *Plays on the Word* is an entirely appropriate title. Apart from the fact that the title is itself a play on words, it is also the case that all the plays in this collection are based firmly on the Word of God. In fact, the principal aim of writing and publishing these pieces is always to communicate the truth of God's Word. I hope that you will find that the material provided here does just that, effectively, with humour, with pace, with dramatic impact and with genuine enjoyment.

Because there is always such a demand for Christmas material we have decided to reprint in this book the four most popular Christmas sketches from two of the earlier books. This is to ensure that these valued resources continue to be available as earlier books inevitably go out of print. This collection therefore contains eight pieces which could be used during the Christmas period.

Each of the sketches in this collection is designed to have a performing time of between 10 and 20 minutes. Quotations from the Bible are taken mainly from the New International Version, published in Great Britain by Hodder & Stoughton.

Derek Haylock

Using Christian Drama

My hero is Jeremiah. Well, we all have our little idiosyncrasies. It's just that communicating God's truth through short pieces of drama seems to me to be such an obvious and natural way of going about it, that it was very encouraging when I came across someone in the Bible who did just that. And a prophet, no less. What is more, a major prophet.

When Jeremiah had to communicate to the people of Judah, for example, that God was going to bring judgement upon them for their idolatry and disobedience, he didn't just say it; he took an audience of elders along to the local potter, and told them to watch while he bought a clay pot, held it up in front of them, and then smashed it to pieces on the ground (Jeremiah 19). An effective little piece of symbolic drama. On other occasions he acted out, for instance, the fascinating dramas of 'hiding the linen belt' (Jeremiah 13) and 'the purchase of the field' (Jeremiah 32). And the scripts were written by God. What more justification do I need?

Of course, analogy, metaphor, and parable are all used substantially throughout the Bible, not least by the Lord Jesus himself. Indeed, the communion service, the central act of Christian worship, is itself a small piece of theatre, in which ordinary actions are used to convey and experience deep spiritual truths.

Drama, as a means of communicating Christian truth can similarly be extremely effective, as the audience are led to identify with the characters, emotions and situations portrayed by the performers. Making contact and establishing a rapport with an audience is, of course, an essential prerequisite for communication. For many people, left cold by a conventional sermon or talk, a short piece of lively and humorous drama can break down barriers and help them to be open to the challenge of God's word.

This book contains therefore a number of pieces which seek to communicate to an adult or mixed-age audience some important aspects of the gospel. *Don't Care, Won't Care, Couldn't Care Less*, for example, challenges the audience to recognise that polluting the environment is also a question of spoiling God's good creation; *A Window in the Diary* challenges those who just turn up at church for Christmas and ignore the Lord for the rest of the year; *The Shepherd and the Psychiatrist* should make the audience think about the implications for them as individuals if the story of the birth of Christ is actually true.

We have also found drama to be an effective way of presenting a Bible story to groups of young people. I hope that readers who teach the Word of God to young people, in churches or youth groups, will find, for example, the four sketches under the general heading *Here is the News* a useful resource. The idea of using a TV news broadcast to report on some biblical events is simple, but it has great potential for humour and impact. I hope that readers will be able to take the structure and the characters provided here to write their own scripts for other Bible stories.

There is value also for the performers. Particularly when involving young people in drama, there is much potential for at least three aspects of learning: retention, understanding and empathy.

First, participation in the acting out of a Bible story, especially if this can be done in a way which they actually enjoy and with plenty of energy, undoubtedly helps youngsters at the simplest level of actually remembering the Bible story. If the piece also includes the repetition of significant verses of scripture, then again the youngsters' involvement will facilitate their retention of those verses.

Second, the performers are enabled to understand better the passage of scripture being presented, by being involved with it. They can be helped to understand the issues and the implications for themselves. Active involvement leads to understanding much more frequently than mere listening. Young people can often appreciate much more clearly why people did what they did and reacted how they reacted, when they themselves have acted out the roles in question. Significant concepts, such as forgiveness and reconciliation, which sadly may be too rarely experienced in youngsters' own lives, can sometimes be experienced and understood better through participation in drama. The piece entitled *Christian Olympics* in this collection, for example, has been useful for discussing with youngsters what it means to 'persevere' in the Christian life and to 'keep your eyes fixed on Jesus'. *Follow the Leader* gives young people an experience which enables them to talk about peer pressure and the courage needed to stand out from the crowd and to be different by following Jesus.

Third, there is the notion of 'empathy'. This refers to the possibility of identifying with the interests and attitudes of another person or group. By participating in drama, sometimes we can achieve this much deeper level of appreciation of the motives and emotions of the characters involved: almost to the point that we feel as though we are at one with the individual portrayed. To be at one with the central figure of the Word of God, is, of course, the way of salvation.

Performance to other people is not essential for the above kinds of learning to take place. But, I do find that many young people do positively enjoy performing, although this is sometimes not the case during the more sensitive years of adolescence. Giving a performance – to parents, to the rest of the school, to the church, and so on – gives some purposefulness to the activity and increases the motivation to make the production as good as possible. Consequently, all the pieces in this book have been written for performance, either to groups of young people, such as in a school assembly, or to a mixed-age audience, for example, in a church family service. In a church context, the opportunity for young people to participate in a family service through a piece of lively drama, which they themselves enjoy, is one way of bringing the young people to the centre of the church's life and of making them feel accepted.

With children, I have found it most useful to write material which involves all available children, for example, a whole class of, say, thirty, rather than simply writing plays which can only involve a handful of children with particular acting ability. I have also always worked on the assumption that rehearsal time is limited. If these two criteria match the reader's requirements, then you may find useful such pieces as: *Whoever* and *The Flaming Fiery Furnace*, which employ a Chorus and which make much use of repetition; and *Light on the Road to Damascus*, which is just a Bible story told in the form of rhyming doggerel, to which a group of children mime.

Writing Christian Drama

People often ask me how I do it. Well, I think it's roughly along the lines described below, although I certainly do not work through these stages systematically in order every time. However it may be that this framework will be of some help to others who wish to have a go at writing their own Christian drama.

1 What is the occasion?

I normally start with a requirement or request to produce a piece of drama for a particular occasion, such as a school assembly, a special service at church, a young people's houseparty, an evening at the youth club etc. I make sure I know the kind of occasion for which the piece is intended and set out to produce something appropriate. A rip-roaring pantomime would hardly be the thing for a Good Friday church service, for example. The situation in which the piece will be performed will also impose limitations - for example, whether all speakers will need amplification and the availability of microphones.

2 What performers are available?

From the outset I must know what number, age and ability of performers I am writing for. If I need something for a large group of children or young people to perform, then some device for involving as many as possible in non-demanding rôles, such as a Chorus, must be built into the script. If I have a few youngsters with acting ability then I can write something which also allows them some central rôles, with a few lines to learn. These considerations will determine the format of the piece, such as whether it uses narrators and readers, whether it involves a group performing actions in unison, or whether it can be more of a conventional play. Then, I must know how much time is available for rehearsal and what is reasonable to expect in terms of actors learning lines.

3 Who is the audience?

Clearly it makes a difference to what I write if I am preparing something for an adult audience, a mixed-age audience, or an audience of children. It is also clearly important to know whether the audience consists mainly of committed church-goers, or those very much on the edge of Christianity. These factors will affect the kind of message I will try to communicate through the drama.

4   Decide on the main point

Often, I find it helps my thinking enormously to clarify precisely what is the single, main point which the drama should communicate. Even if the purpose is simply to retell an event from the Bible, I try to decide what is the most significant point in the story. This focuses my thinking and prevents me from cluttering up the piece with too much detail and keeps the piece moving towards making the point in question. The example of Jesus's parables is helpful here - normally they contain one major point of great significance and just enough incidental detail to keep the audience interested.

5   Study the Word of God

Before writing a piece, I spend some time becoming thoroughly familiar with the relevant passages of scripture, looking into commentaries for useful background information, and hunting through *The NIV Complete Concordance* (Hodder & Stoughton 1981) to locate other verses of scripture which might support the main point which I wish the drama to make. I always try to incorporate some words of scripture in some way into each piece of drama. This is one way of ensuring that not everything I write is complete rubbish.

6   A creative idea

This is the tricky bit. From somewhere you have to get hold of a novel, creative idea or concept, on which to hang the piece of drama. Once I've got this, the whole thing often just flows along quite easily. Once I had thought of sending one of the shepherds to a psychiatrist (See *The Shepherd and the Psychiatrist*), for example, the play seemed to write itself. I often get these ideas whilst lying in the bath, or cycling to work, sometimes not even consciously thinking about the piece of drama I am trying to create. I know the occasion, the performers, the audience, the main point and the Bible teaching – now I give my mind a chance to work on these and come up with some unusual or original association. You can even try associating things at random and see what happens.

7   How is it going to finish?

I always decide this very early on in the writing process. I must admit it's difficult sometimes and I wish I had available Monty Python's large foot to come crashing down to bring things to a conclusion. Especially with a short piece of drama, a crisp, poignant or unexpected ending is essential.

8   Use humour

I try to pack plenty of humour in, particularly early on in the sketches. This helps to break down the audience's resistance and to make contact with them. Much of the humour I use is verbal, rather than slapstick, and, alright, I'll admit it, most of it is pretty corny. But it does seem to work.

9   Establish characters quickly

In a short piece of drama, it is essential that characters establish themselves very quickly. This will mean exaggerating their attributes, both in the writing and in the performing. There is not a lot of room for subtlety in a short, punchy piece of drama. If possible, I try to give characters some little quirk, which helps to identify them.

10   Rehearse and edit

Once the piece is written, I spend a lot of time going through it and editing it carefully. Most pieces of drama are too long rather than too short. I try to cut out anything which slows down the pace too much. For this reason, I avoid long speeches by one individual, for example, using two narrators rather than one in some of the pieces. I always read each piece out loud and get someone else to read it with me, just to check that the words have a natural speech rhythm to them, that they sound well, not just read well. Then, once we start rehearsing, I am always prepared to edit the piece further. Invariably, I find that practical considerations, such as the time it takes to perform certain actions, will necessitate some re-writing. The key to good writing is editing. A word-processor is essential.

Whoever

Bible Base
Mainly John 6.37; but also references to: Luke 2.8-20; Matthew 2.1-12; John 3.1-21; John 4.1-26; Luke 19.1-10; Matthew 8.1-4; Luke 23.39-43; Luke 18.15-17.

Introduction
This is a piece designed to involve a large number of children for a Christmas event, although it could be used at any time. The main point of the piece is that Jesus really does welcome everyone of us, whatever we are like, whether cognoscenti, like the wise men, or hoi polloi, like the shepherds! His dealings with people throughout his life showed this clearly to be the case. The sketch shows the range of people who came to the Lord Jesus and, as he promises, were not turned away.

Cast
Narrators 1 and 2
Shepherds 1 and 2
Wise Men 1 and 2
Nicodemus
Samaritan Woman
Zacchaeus
Outcast
Thief
Chorus (all available children)
Audience!

(During the course of the piece the group of Followers, starting with just the shepherds, gradually builds up, eventually encompassing the entire cast. The Followers go round and round the hall, picking up more followers each time as they cross the stage. The piece relies very heavily on repetition, so that the children taking part do not have to learn complicated lines. The repeated sequence should be done very rhythmically. By the end of the piece the audience should have picked up the idea of the sequence of repeated lines and are required to join in. They should be warned of this in advance, and their lines can be written on a series of cue cards which someone

holds up when required. Narrators 1 and 2 stand on opposite corners at the front of the stage. The Chorus are lined up along the back.)

Narrator 1 Jesus said:

Narrator 2 Whoever comes to me

Narrator 1 I will never turn away.

Narrator 2 It started with his birth,

Narrator 1 In Bethlehem.

(Shepherds enter from left.)

Narrator 2 Some scruffy shepherds on a hillside,

Narrator 1 Told by an angel to go to meet a new-born King.

Chorus Pooh, smell the sheep!
(*Hold noses*)

Shepherd 1 Can we go to Jesus?

Chorus What you?

Shepherd 2 Will we be welcome?

Chorus Welcome you?

Narrator 1 Jesus said:

Narrator 2 Whoever comes to me

Narrator 1 I will never turn away.

Shepherds What never?

Chorus No, never!

Shepherds Whoever?

Chorus Whoever!

Shepherd 1 *(To Shepherd 2)*
Whoever comes to him he will never turn away!

Shepherd 2 Come on then, let's go! To Jesus!
(*Exit right*)

Narrator 1 Some time later some wise men came from the East

(Wise men enter from left.)

Narrator 2 Looking for Jesus.

Narrator 1 They had seen his star,

Narrator 2	And were come to worship the new-born king.
Chorus	Foreigners! *(Aghast gesture)*
Wise Man 1	Can we go to Jesus?
Chorus	What you?
Wise Man 2	Will we be welcome?
Chorus	Welcome you?
Narrator 1	Jesus said:
Narrator 2	Whoever comes to me
Narrator 1	I will never turn away.
Wise Men	What never?
Chorus	No, never!
Wise Men	Whoever?
Chorus	Whoever!

(Enter Shepherds from left.)

Shepherds	*(To Wise Men)* Whoever comes to him he will never turn away!
Wise Men	Come on then, let's go! To Jesus!

(Wise Men and Shepherds exit right.)

Narrator 1	Some years later,
Narrator 2	A Jewish leader,
Narrator 1	Nicodemus by name,

(Enter Nicodemus from left.)

Narrator 2	He came to Jesus by night.
Narrator 1	A religious man,
Narrator 2	But needing the new life that only Jesus could give.
Chorus	A Pharisee! *(Snooty gesture)*
Nicodemus	Can I go to Jesus?
Chorus	What you?
Nicodemus	Will I be welcome?

Chorus   Welcome you?

Narrator 1 Jesus said:

Narrator 2 Whoever comes to me

Narrator 1 I will never turn away.

Nicodemus   What never?

Chorus   No, never!

Nicodemus   Whoever?

Chorus   Whoever!

(Enter Shepherds and Wise Men – the Followers – from left.)

Followers   *(To Nicodemus)*
                Whoever comes to him he will never turn away!

Nicodemus   Come on then, let's go! To Jesus!

(Shepherds, Wise Men and Nicodemus exit right.)

Narrator 1 One day, Jesus met a woman by a well.

(Enter Samaritan Woman from left, carrying a large jug.)

Narrator 2 A Samaritan,

Narrator 1 Living with a man who wasn't her husband.

Chorus   Disgraceful!
                (Shake heads and tut)

Woman   Can I go to Jesus?

Chorus   What you?

Woman   Will I be welcome?

Chorus   Welcome you?

Narrator 1 Jesus said:

Narrator 2 Whoever comes to me

Narrator 1 I will never turn away.

Woman   What never?

Chorus   No, never!

Woman   Whoever?

Chorus   Whoever!

18

(Enter Shepherds, Wise Men and Nicodemus – the Followers – from left.)

Followers   *(To Samaritan Woman)*
Whoever comes to him he will never turn away!

Woman   Come on then, let's go! To Jesus!

(Shepherds, Wise Men, Nicodemus and Samaritan Woman exit right.)

Narrator 1   And so it went on throughout his life.

(The four Characters – Zacchaeus, Mary Magdalene, Outcast, Thief – enter one by one from left.)

Narrator 2   A tax collector called Zacchaeus.
(Chorus hiss.)

Narrator 1   A sinful woman called Mary Magdalene.
(Chorus gasp.)

Narrator 2   A man with a horrible skin disease that made him an outcast.

Chorus   Unclean! Unclean!
(With appropriate gesture)

Narrator 1   And even a common criminal hanging beside him on a cross.

Chorus   Thief!
(Pointing accusingly)

Characters   Can we go to Jesus?

Chorus   What, you?

Characters   Will we be welcome?

Chorus   Welcome you?

Narrator 1   Jesus said:

Narrator 2   Whoever comes to me

Narrator 1   I will never turn away.

Characters   What never?

Chorus   No, never!

Characters   Whoever?

Chorus   Whoever!

(Enter Shepherds, Wise Men, Nicodemus and Samaritan Woman – the Followers – from left.)

Followers   *(To the four Characters)*
Whoever comes to him he will never turn away!

Characters   Come on then, let's go! To Jesus!

(Followers, including now the four Characters, exit right.)

Narrator 1   They even brought children to Jesus.

(Chorus step forward.)

Narrator 2   The disciples tried to stop them.

(Narrators hold up hands to signal stop – Chorus turn backs on audience as if to walk away.)

Narrator 1   But Jesus said:

Narrator 2   Let the children come to me.

(Chorus face front again.)

Chorus   Can we go to Jesus?

(Narrators encourage audience to join in – use cue cards.)

Audience   What you?

Chorus   Will we be welcome?

Audience   Welcome you?

Narrator 1   Jesus said:

Narrator 2   Whoever comes to me

Narrator 1   I will never turn away.

Chorus   What never?

Audience   No, never!

Chorus   Whoever?

Audience   Whoever!

(Enter all the Followers from left.)

Followers   *(To Chorus)*
Whoever comes to him he will never turn away!

Chorus   Come on then, let's go! To Jesus!

(Followers, including the Chorus, exit right.)

Narrator 1   Is there anyone else then?

Narrator 2   Well . . .
(Pointing to audience)
. . . there's that lot out there?

Narrator 1   What them?

Audience   Can we go to Jesus?

Narrators   What you?

Audience   Will we be welcome?

Narrators   Welcome you?

Narrator 1   Well . . . Jesus did say:

Narrator 2   Whoever comes to me

Narrator 1   I will never turn away.

Audience   What never?

Narrators   No, never!

Audience   Whoever?

Narrators   Whoever!

(All the Followers, including now the Chorus, come running onto the stage, from left.)

Followers   *(To audience)*
Whoever comes to him he will never turn away! So, come on then, let's go! To Jesus!

Rejection[1]

Bible Base
Micah 5.2; Luke 2.4-7; John 1.10-11; Isaiah 53.3,7; John 19.18; Luke 17.25; Luke 9.22; I Peter 2.4.

Introduction
This is a serious piece of symbolic mime, with readings of various verses from the Bible, music and sound effects. It is designed for children to perform in a Christmas service, although it could equally well be used at Easter. It aims to show that Jesus is rejected by many today just as there was no room for him in the inn at Bethlehem, and just as during his adult life on earth many rejected him, even to the point of crucifixion.

Cast
Reader
Nine Citizens
Mary
Joseph
Jesus

(Some appropriate instrumental music, such as O Little Town of Bethlehem *or* There is a Green Hill, *either played on a keyboard or pre-recorded, is required. This fades in and out during the first half of the piece. Required for the last part is a recording of a sequence of modern-day sound effects, such as traffic noise, TV advertisements, computer bleeps, telephone ringing, pop music, TV news headline, and a football commentary. The citizens can be dressed in simple modern-day clothes, with Mary and Joseph in traditional historical costume. Jesus should wear an appropriate costume which will enable the audience to identify him. The impact of this piece relies on carefully orchestrated movement and sudden*

---

1   An earlier version of this piece, under the title *No Room*, is published in *Drama Toolkit* (edited by G & R Lamont, Bible Society, 1989).

silences at dramatic moments. The stage is empty apart from a ramp or steps leading to a raised platform at the back centre.)

Reader   But you, O Bethlehem, in the land of Judah, though you are small among the clans of Judah, out of you will come for me one who will be ruler over Israel, whose origins are from of old, from ancient times.

(The music – e.g. O Little Town of Bethlehem *– begins, as the nine citizens march on slowly, forming a straight line across the centre of the stage. They carry placards, which, when they turn to face the audience, will be seen to spell out B-E-T-H-L-E-H-E-M. Mary and Joseph enter.)*

Reader   Joseph went up from the town of Nazareth in Galilee, to Judea, to Bethlehem the town of David.

(Citizens turn to face the audience, spelling out the name BETHLEHEM.)

Reader   He went there to register with Mary, who was pledged to be married to him and who was expecting a child. While they were there, the time came for the baby to be born. But there was no room for them in the inn.

(Mary and Joseph head towards the line of citizens. The one on the extreme right of the line takes one pace to the right, thus making a gap in the line. As Mary and Joseph move to go through this gap the next citizen takes a pace to the right and closes it. This then opens up a new gap in the line, which in turn is closed by the next citizen. So, as Mary and Joseph make their way along the line, each gap that opens to them is closed. As each citizen moves they turn their placard round to reveal messages written on the reverse side, such as, NO ROOM, SORRY, FULL UP, TRY ELSEWHERE, NO VACANCIES, NOT HERE, APOLOGIES, TOO BUSY, PACKED OUT. Finally, Mary and Joseph slowly walk away, and exit. Music down as the Reader begins.)

Reader   *(As Mary and Joseph exit)*
And she gave birth to her first-born, a son. She wrapped him in cloths and placed him in a manger, because there was no room for them in the inn.

(Music up)

(The citizens kneel and lower their placards to the ground. Jesus enters and stands behind the kneeling citizens, who have their backs towards him.)

(Music down)

Reader   *(As Jesus enters)*
He was in the world, and though the world was made through him, the world did not recognise him. He came to that which was his own, but his own did not receive him.

(Music up – change to something like There is a Green Hill. *The citizens stand and face Jesus for a couple of seconds. Then they turn their backs on him.)*

Reader   The Son of Man must suffer many things and be rejected by this generation.

(During the following reading they walk slowly backwards, pushing Jesus up the ramp. Finally he reaches the platform and stands there above the crowd.)

Reader   He was despised and rejected, a man of sorrows and familiar with suffering. He was oppressed and afflicted, yet he did not open his mouth; he was led like a lamb to the slaughter, and as a sheep before her shearers is silent, so he did not open his mouth.

(Jesus, now on the platform, turns his back on the audience.)

They crucified him.

(The music stops abruptly. Jesus snaps into a crucified posture. The citizens freeze. There is silence for about ten seconds. Then the citizens walk off slowly. Jesus turns and walks down the ramp to a position centre stage, while the following verse is read.)

Reader   The Son of Man must suffer many things and be rejected by the elders, chief priests and teachers of the law, and he must be killed – but on the third day be raised to life.

(Jesus raises his hands in invitation.)

Reader   Come to him, the living Stone, rejected by men, but chosen by God and precious to him.

(The modern-day sound effects are heard – they continue now until the drumbeat – the citizens march on again, this time more quickly. They busy themselves with various things, such as reading The Radio Times, *disco-dancing to music on their headphones, jogging, making telephone calls, shopping, football, etc. The stage must be full of activity and noise. The crowd just ignores Jesus standing in the middle of it all with his arms outstretched. Gradually they crowd round him, still ignoring him, move into a huddle and push him out. As he falls out of the crowd, forward onto the stage floor, there is a dramatic, loud drumbeat. The crowd freezes and there is silence. After a few seconds Jesus slowly picks himself up from the floor. He looks sadly behind him at the crowd. They do not move. Slowly and deliberately, he turns and looks at the audience. Then, lowering his head, he walks solemnly off the stage, through the audience, and exits from the building. Blackout.)*

The Wallies Guide to Christmas

Bible Base
Luke 2.6-20; Matthew 2.11; John 1.10-14.

Introduction
This sketch is derived from a Christmas catalogue from a well-know
High Street store. The catalogue was based on the theme
'Christmas is . . . '. The aim of this sketch is to remind us that the
world's view of what Christmas is leaves out one vital ingredient –
the Lord Jesus!

Cast
A, B, C - Wallies salespersons
D - Member of the audience
E - Christian commentator
F - Reader from the Bible

*(A, B and C take up their positions centre stage. Each has a
Christmas catalogue from a well-known store in their hands. They
can read their sales patter from photocopies of the script stapled
inside the catalogues. E stands stage left, looking away, but
occasionally turning to comment on the Wallies sales pitch. D is
seated in the audience, but stands up from time to time to say,
'Excuse me', sitting down again when ignored. F is seated stage right,
reading from the Bible. A, B and C subject us to a hard sell . . .)*

A	In the Wallies Christmas catalogue you will find . . .
B	. . . the answer to the question:
C	What is Christmas all about?
D	*(Stands up, raises hand)* Excuse me . . .
A	*(Ignoring D, who then sits down – this happens repeatedly.)* And so, ladies and gentlemen . . .
B	. . . boys and girls . . .
C	. . . we bring you . . .
A	. . . the Wallies Guide to Christmas!

D	Excuse me, but . . .
A	Wallies have great ideas for a great Christmas.
B	Whatever you want for Christmas, you'll find it . . .
C	. . . at Wallies.
A	What makes a happy Christmas?
B	The Wallies catalogue has the answer . . .
E	*(Looking briefly in their direction)* What about the Bible?

(A, B, C look at E puzzled, but then decide to ignore E here and elsewhere.)

A	At the Wallies store we know what you want for Christmas. Because Christmas is all about . . .
F	*(Reading from the Bible)* 'The time came for the baby to be born, and Mary gave birth to her firstborn, a son.'

(A,B, C look at F puzzled, but decide to ignore this and subsequent interventions.)

A	As we were saying . . .
B	Christmas is . . .
C	Decorations!
D	Excuse me . . .
A	See the Wallies green and silver tinsel artificial Christmas trees, only £7.99 . . .
B	. . . and the Wallies plastic holly bunch, only 99 pence . . .
C	. . . and the six assorted shatterproof baubles in all your favourite luminous colours, £1.29.
A	Yes, you can make your home look like a palace this Christmas . . .
B	. . . with your Wallies Christmas decorations your home will look like a place fit for a king!
E	And what sort of place would be fit for a King, I wonder?

F	'And she wrapped him in strips of cloth and laid him in a manger, because there was no room for them in the inn.'
A	Christmas is . . .
B	Entertainment!
D	Excuse me . . . .
C	Yes, the Christmas angels in the Wallies Christmas catalogue are here to announce the good news . . .
B	. . . that we can bring you . . .
C	. . . the best in Wallies entertainment this Christmas . . .
A	. . . action packed videos, like James Bond in *A View to a Kill*.
C	*The Texas Chainsaw Massacre.*
A	And Julie Andrews in *Mary Poppins*!

(Gasps of horror)

B	Yes, there's no need to have a dull Christmas if you're a Wallies customer!
E	Is that really the good news of Christmas?
F	'The angel said to the shepherds: do not be afraid, I bring you good news of great joy that will be for all the people.'
C	And Christmas for Wallies is first and foremost . . . .
A	. . . something for the children!
E	I thought it was actually about one particular child?
F	'Today in the town of David a Saviour has been born to you; he is Christ the Lord.'
B	Yes, Christmas is kids!
D	Excuse me . . .
C	A Wallies Christmas will bring you . . .
A	A Phaser Force Two Battle Game, £19.95.
B	A Thundercats Sword of Omens, £4.99.
C	An Action force Snowcat Missile Carrier, £9.95.

E	Happy Christmas! *(With irony)* And a peaceful new year.
F	'Suddenly a great company of the heavenly host appeared with the angel, praising God and saying, "Glory to God in the highest and peace to men on earth"'.
A	Christmas is . . .
B	. . . looking smart!
D	Excuse me . . .
C	Take a look at the Wallies range of colourful co-ordinated clothes.
A	Look smart this Christmas!
B	Wrap yourself in a Wallies bright red tassel hat, £1.50, with matching scarf, £2.25.
E	I don't believe this!
F	'This will be a sign to you. You will find a baby wrapped in strips of cloth, and lying in a mangor.'
C	So hurry now to your local Wallies store . . .
A	And find just what you're looking for this Christmas.
E	What are we looking for this Christmas?
F	'So the shepherds hurried off and found Mary and Joseph, and the baby . . . '
B	Spread the word! Tell your friends that Wallies have the answer to all their needs this Christmas. They will be amazed!
E	*(Sarcastically)* Yes, it is quite amazing . . .
F	'. . . When they had seen him they spread the word concerning what has been told them about this child, and all who heard it were amazed at what the shepherds said to them.'
A	Christmas is . . .
B	. . . gifts!

C	Don't forget those you love this Christmas.
D	Excuse me . . . .
A	Buy them a gift at Wallies.
C	A present for Mum?
A	How about the Bloke and Digger variable-speed hammer drill? Only £37.95.
B	And for Dad?
A	A matching oven glove and apron set, with the exclusive Wallies cherry blossom motif. Only £7.99.
C	Yes, wise men get all their Christmas gifts at Wallies!
E	*(Thoughtfully)* If I were a wise man, I would do my part.
F	'They bowed down and worshipped him. Then they opened up their treasures and presented him with gifts . . .'
C	Give a Wallies gift to someone who loves you this Christmas.
E	'Yet what I can I give him . . .'
A	Yes, we have thought of everything you need for a wonderful Christmas.
E	Everything?
B	We haven't forgotten anything!
E	No, not much! *(Exit)*
D	Excuse me . . .
C	That's the world of Wallies, where wishes come true!
A	Remember then, the Wallies Christmas message!
B	Christmas is . . .
C	Decorations!
A	Entertainment!
B	Looking smart!
C	Kids!

A   . . . and gifts!

D   *(Really shouting now!)*
               Excuse me!

(Everyone stops and looks at D.)

D   *(Calmly)*
               But what about Jesus?

A,B & C   *(Together)*
               Jesus?
               (They look frantically in their catalogues, then slowly turn to listen as F reads.)

F   'The Word became flesh and lived for a while among us. He was in the world, and though the world was made through him, the world did not recognise him. He came to that which was his own, but his own did not receive him. Yet to all who did receive him, to those who believed in his name, he gave the right to become the children of God.'

(F gets up, looks across at A, B and C, leaves Bible on the chair and exits. A goes across and picks up the Bible. A shows something in it to B and C. They look at each other, then all three quietly tear up their Wallies catalogues and walk off.)

A   *(Turning and addressing the audience just before leaving the stage)*
               On second thoughts, don't be a Wally this Christmas!

The Flaming Fiery Furnace

Bible Base
Daniel 3.1-30; Isaiah 43.1-4; Matthew 28.20.

Introduction
This sketch is designed to enable a large number of children to participate in presenting the exciting story of Shadrach, Meshach and Abednego being thrown into the flaming fiery furnace (Daniel chapter 3). The main point to be drawn from this incident is not that God promises always to deliver us unharmed from our own fiery furnaces, but that he does promise to be in there with us. This is brought out by appropriate Bible verses at the end of the sketch.

The piece employs a Chorus, a useful device for enabling as many children as are available in the group to participate. Their contributions consist mainly of three sequences which are repeated frequently – the repetition in the sketch is an important factor in its effectiveness, so these sequences must always be done very rhythmically. The idea of repeating again and again the long list of musical instruments actually occurs in the original version in Daniel 3, possibly as a way of poking fun at the King's edict. There is plenty of humour in the sketch, including the idea of the recitation of the list of musical instruments gradually slipping into the Cornish Floral Dance!

Cast
Shadrach
Meshach
Abednego
King Nebuchadnezzar
Herald
Musician
Carrier of Postcard
Narrators 1 and 2 (could be adults)
Chorus (all available children)

(The Chorus, including Shadrach, Meshach and Abednego, are lined up along the back of the stage. At least the three young men

should be in 'historical' costume. Narrators should be on opposite sides, preferably off-stage, but visible to the audience. There is a throne and a small table stage left, where the King will sit.)

Narrator 1   Once upon a time,

Narrator 2   In Babylon,

Narrator 1   There were three young men,

Narrator 2   Who believed in the one true God.

Narrator 1   This is the story of those three young men:

(The next sequence occurs repeatedly in the sketch. It should be done very rhythmically. As their names are called the three young men should step forward dramatically and adopt a characteristic pose.)

Narrator 2   Num-ber-one.

Chorus   Shad-rach!

(Shadrach leaps forward from the Chorus and stands with right arm raised and right leg thrust forward.)

Narrator 2   Num-ber-two.

Chorus   Me-shach!

(Meshach leaps forward from the Chorus and stands with left arm raised and left leg thrust forward.)

Narrator 2   Num-ber-three.

Chorus   A-beeeeeed-ne-go!

(Abednego leaps forward from the Chorus and stands between the other two with legs apart and both arms raised. They hold these positions.)

Narrator 1   Now here comes the King!

Narrator 2   Nebuchadnezzar!

(Shadrach, Meshach and Abednego leap back into the chorus)

Chorus   *(Imitating trumpets)*
                Da-da-da-da-da-daaaa!

(Enter King, stage right, gesturing royally. Chorus bow accordingly.)

Narrator 1   Now the King had ordered that a gold statue be made and set up where everyone could see it.

(King points out in direction of audience. Chorus look in this direction, point, and gradually raise their eyes and fingers, higher and higher during the following sequence.)

Narrator 2 It was huge.

Narrator 1 It was enormous.

Narrator 2 It was vast.

Narrator 1 It was gigantic.

Narrator 2 It was magnificent.

Narrator 1 It was immense.

Narrator 2 *(Getting more and more carried away)*
It was macroscopic, thumping-great, stupendous, giant-size, megalithic . . .

Narrator *(Anti-climactic)*
Quite big actually.

Chorus Wow!

Narrator 2 King Nebuchadnezzar issued a decree.

(King takes his seat, unrolls a scroll and writes.)

Narrator 1 *(Very serious)*
Everyone must bow down and worship the King's statue,

Narrator 2 Whenever they hear the sound of the trumpet.

Narrator 1 Oboe.

Narrator 2 Harp.

Narrator 1 Lyre.

Narrator 2 Whenever they hear the distant drone . . .

(Slipping into the rhythm of the Cornish floral dance, and gradually becoming jollier . . .)

Narrator 1 . . . of the cornet, clarinet . . .

Chorus Big trombone.

Narrator 1 Fiddle, cello . . .

Chorus Big bass drum.

Narrator 1 Bassoon, flute . . .

Chorus   And eu-pho-ni-um!

(The above sequence occurs a number of times and should always be done with the same rhythm. The Chorus should mime playing the big trombone, the big bass drum and the euphonium. When this sequence recurs later, the audience can be encouraged to join in with the Chorus.)

Narrator 2   Or else . . .

Narrator 1   . . . be thrown . . . into . . .

Chorus   *(All point dramatically stage right)*
        . . . the flaming fiery furnace!
        (Gasp)

Narrator 2   The King's herald took the decree from the King. Standing in front of the statue
        (Appropriate action)
        he proclaimed in a loud voice:

Herald   *(Stepping forward and reading the decree, like a town crier)*
        Oyos, oycs! Hear ye the decree of King Nebuchadnezzar of Babylon! Everyone must bow down and worship the King's statue, whenever they hear the sound of the trumpet, oboe, harp and lyre.

(As before . . .)

Narrator 2   Whenever they hear the distant drone . . .

Narrator 1   . . . of the cornet, clarinet . . .

Chorus   Big trombone.

Narrator 1   Fiddle, cello . . .

Chorus   Big bass drum.

Narrator 1   Bassoon, flute . . .

Chorus   And eu-pho-ni-um!

Herald   Or else . . . be thrown . . . into . . .

Chorus   *(All point dramatically stage right)*
        . . . the flaming fiery furnace!
        (Gasp)

Herald	Call the entire company of the loyal band of the King's musicians!
Narrator 1	*(Calling)* The entire company of the loyal band of the King's musicians!

(Everyone gestures dramatically in one direction, stage right, as though awaiting the arrival of a grand procession. One small child enters, laden with every kind of available musical instrument!)

Narrator 2	*(To Narrator 1)* Is that it?
Narrator 1	Sorry, that's all we could afford . . . but she's very good.
Herald	Let the entire company of the loyal band of the King's musicians be heard. Sound the trumpet!

(Musician acts confused, wondering which instrument to play.)

Narrator 1	Oboe.
Narrator 2	Harp.
Narrator 1	Lyre.
Narrator 2	Let them hear the distant drone . . .
Narrator 1	. . . of the cornet, clarinet.
Chorus	Big trombone.
Narrator 1	Fiddle, cello . . .
Chorus	Big bass drum.
Narrator 1	Bassoon, flute . . .
Chorus	And eu-pho-ni-um!

(Musician raises one instrument to lips and pretends to play – there is a blast of loud pre-recorded music: we found a short extract of jazz trumpet-playing to be very effective! All members of the Chorus bow down, except Shadrach, Meshach and Abednego. They turn their backs to the audience, away from the direction of the statue. When the musician has finished playing she bows down as well.)

Narrator 2	But three young men did not bow down.
Narrator 1	Who were they?

Narrator 2   Num-ber-one.

(The three spin round in turn and take their characteristic positions as before.)

Chorus   *(Pointing)*
Shad-rach!

Narrator 2   Num-ber-two.

Chorus   *(Pointing)*
Me-shach!

Narrator 2   Num-ber-three.

Chorus   *(Pointing)*
A-beeeeeed-ne-go!

Narrator 1   Then some rotten sneaks came and told the King.

(Chorus get up and two of them go across to the King. They mime appropriately. Musician exits.)

Narrator 2   Three young men did not bow down and worship your statue, O King. When they heard the sound of the trumpet . . .

Narrator 1   Oboe.

Narrator 2   Harp.

Narrator 1   Lyre.

Narrator 2   When they heard the distant drone . . .

Narrator 1   . . . of the Cornet, clarinet . . .

Chorus   Big trombone.

Narrator 1   Fiddle, cello . . .

Chorus   Big bass drum.

Narrator 1   Bassoon, flute . . .

Chorus   And eu-pho-ni-um!

King   *(Furious, leaping to his feet)*
What! Who are these men who dare to disobey my decree?

(The two members of the chorus go and bring the three men to the King, one at a time, co-ordinated with the following sequence.)

Narrator 1	Well, there's . . .
Narrator 2	Num-ber-one.
Chorus	Shad-rach! *(They throw him forward)*
Narrator 2	Num-ber-two.
Chorus	Me-shach! *(They throw him forward)*
Narrator 2	Num-ber-three.
Chorus	A-beeeeeed-ne-go! *(They throw him forward)*
King	*(To S, M and A)* Did you bow down to my statue?
S, M & A	Nope!
King	Did you hear the sound of the trumpet?
Narrator 1	Oboe.
Narrator 2	Harp.
Narrator 1	Lyre.

(S, M and A do a little dance, as the sequence continues, finishing up in their characteristic positions, to coincide with their answer . . .)

Narrator 2	Did you hear the distant drone . . .
Narrator 1	. . . of the cornet, clarinet.
Chorus	Big trombone.
Narrator 1	Fiddle, cello . . .
Chorus	Big bass drum.
Narrator 1	Bassoon, flute . . .
Chorus	And eu-pho-ni-um!
S, M & A	Yep!
King	In that case . . . you will be thrown . . . into . . .
Chorus	*(Pointing dramatically as before)* . . . the flaming fiery furnace! *(Gasp)*

(The King sits.)

Narrator 2   But Shadrach, Meshach and Abednego answered:

(They mime appropriately, pointing up to their God, to the furnace, to the statue, and finally gesturing towards the statue dismissively.)

Narrator 1   The living God whom we serve can save us from the flaming fiery furnace. But even if he does not, we will not worship your god, or bow down to your statue.

S, M & A   So there!
(Folding arms defiantly)

Narrator 2   Then the King was really furious.

(Appropriate action by King . . .)

(The Chorus crowd round the edge of the stage, then gradually back away, acting as though they are getting roasted by the fire.)

He ordered his men to heat the flaming fiery furnace seven times hotter than usual.

Narrator 1   And he ordered the three young men to be thrown . . . into . . .

Chorus   *(Pointing dramatically as before)*
. . . the flaming fiery furnace!

(Two members of the Chorus take hold of each of the three young men in turn, and, with appropriate action, throw them off the stage into the furnace.)

Narrator 2   Num-ber-one.

Chorus   Shad-rach!

Narrator 2   Num-ber-two.

Chorus   Me-shach!

Narrator 2   Num-ber-three.

Chorus   A-beeeeeed-ne-go!
(Cheers)

(All the chorus resume their normal position)

Narrator 1   Suddenly the King leapt to his feet in amazement and pointed . . . into . . .

(Appropriate action by King)

Chorus	*(Pointing)* . . . the flaming fiery furnace!
Narrator 2	What could he see?
King	Num-ber-one.
Chorus	Shad-rach!
King	Num-ber-two.
Chorus	Me-shach!
King	Num-ber-three.
Chorus	A-beeeeeed-ne-go!
King	Number four . . . !
Chorus	Number four?
Narrator 1	There were four men walking about, unhurt, . . . in . . .
Chorus	*(Pointing)* . . . the flaming fiery furnace!
Narrator 2	Not three.
Narrator 1	But four.
Narrator 2	Num-ber-one.
Chorus	Shad-rach!
Narrator 2	Num-ber-two.
Chorus	Me-shach!
Narrator 2	Num-ber-three.
Chorus	A-beeeeeed-ne-go!
Narrator 1	But who was number four?
Chorus	Who was number four?
(Pause)	
Narrator 2	Answers on a postcard, please, to . . . *(insert appropriate name and address, e.g. the actual name and the address of the church or school etc.)*
Narrator 1	. . . to arrive by . . . *(insert an appropriate time, e.g. the next hour after the actual time)* on . . . *(insert actual date.)*

(A child comes running in from the back of church, with a postcard and hands it to Narrator 1.)

Narrator 1 That was quick!
(Reads)
"This is what the Lord says: Fear not, for I have redeemed you. I have summoned you by name. You are mine. When you pass through the waters, I will be with you. And when you pass through the rivers, they will not sweep over you. When you walk through the fire, you will not be burned. For I am the Lord your God. I will be with you. You are precious in my sight."

(Pause. Then appropriate action from the King etc.)

Narrator 2 The King called the three young men out of the furnace. And they were completely unharmed.

Narrator 1 And Nebuchadnezzar was amazed!

King *(Greeting Shadrach)*
I am amazed!

Narrator 2 He was excited!

King *(Greeting Meshach)*
I am excited!

Narrator 1 He was dumbfounded!

King *(Greeting Abednego)*
I am dumbfounded!

Narrator 2 He was forced to undertake a radical restructuring of his theological position.

King I am . . . er, what he said.

Narrator 1 For Nebuchadnezzar had seen the faith of the three young men, who were willing to give up their lives rather than serve any god except their own. So . . .

(King kneels and worships.)

. . . he too gave praise to this one, true, living God, the God of the three young men . . .

(In turn, each of the three faces the audience and adopts their characteristic pose.)

17720

Narrator 2 Num-ber-one.

Chorus Shad-rach!

Narrator 2 Num-ber-two.

Chorus Me-shach!

Narrator 2 Num-ber-three.

Chorus A-beeeeeed-ne-go!

Narrator 1 Who had been with them in . . .

Chorus *(Pointing)*
. . . the flaming fiery furnace!

(Pause)

Narrator 1 And the Lord Jesus said to his disciples:

Chorus "Surely I am with you always, to the very end of the age."

Light on the Road to Damascus

Bible Base
Acts 9.1-31

Introduction

This sketch, recounting the story of Saul's conversion on the road
to Damascus, is an example of a simple, but very effective, method
for producing some drama with a group of children in a very short
time. We have managed to get groups of children aged 8-11 years
to perform this kind of piece at a Family Service with as little as
half an hour's practice a few days beforehand! A whole class of thirty
or more children can participate, but it is simple enough not to be
totally disrupted by various performers failing to turn up on the
day. The text is unashamedly corny doggerel, to which the children
mime. The trick in writing this kind of thing is to get just enough
words into the text to allow for non-stop action by the performers.
The text should be read in a way which maintains the pace of the
action, and which emphasises the corniness of the doggerel. This
may best be done by an adult. Simple costumes should be used, if
possible.

Cast

Reader
Saul (Paul)
Ananias
Messenger
The remaining children are divided into three groups: Saul's gang,
Christians arrested, Christians dispersed.

*(The Reader should be off-stage. The only prop required on the stage
is a stool in one corner, where Ananias will sit. When Saul appears
he is wearing a badge, which says SAUL in big letters – this should
be designed so that at the end of the sketch he can pull off a paper
clip to allow the letter P to drop down and cover the S, thus changing
his name to PAUL.)*

Reader   The news was spreading everywhere,
                "Jesus is risen from the dead!"

(A small group of Christians come on stage, talking together excitedly, gesturing appropriately.)

Many people believed in him,
Responding to what the Apostles said.

In Jerusalem the Christians proclaimed:
"Jesus is Lord! He's alive, it's true!"

(The other Christians gradually come on, listen, join the group, embrace each other, and act excitedly.)

More and more put their trust in him,
And the Christian church just grew and grew.

(Saul enters and stands on the side of the stage, looking angry. The Christians act busily, greeting each other, sharing things, conversing, praising God, praying, etc.)

This made the Jewish leaders cross,
And a man called Saul began to fret:
"These Christians must be stopped at once,
Our own religion is under threat."

(Saul shakes his fist in the direction of the Christians, then signals to his gang – they come on and join him.)

He was determined to destroy the church,
These Christians who said that Christ was risen.
He told his men, "Find these believers,
Arrest them, and throw them into prison!"

(During the next two verses, Saul and his gang go round the stage arresting various Christians, and dragging them off to prison -- i.e. off-stage on one side. About half the group get arrested, while the other half gradually disperse, leaving the stage and spreading themselves around the audience.

He led his men from house to house.
They were an evil gang, tough, but thick.

(Gang make appropriate gestures!)

When they found believers in Jesus Christ,
They dragged them off to the local nick.

Some Christians scattered far and wide,
To escape from Saul's marauding squad.
But everywhere they still proclaimed
The risen Lord Jesus, the Son of God.

(The stage is now cleared of Christians – they have either been arrested or dispersed. The dispersed Christians all come together to one side of the stage, to represent the group meeting in Damascus. A Messenger runs on, whispers in Saul's ear, and points in the direction of the Damascus group.)

Meanwhile Saul had heard about
Some Christians in Damascus town.

(Saul signals to his men and instructs them.)

So he took his gang of ruffians
And set off at once to hunt them down.

(They march around the stage a couple of times.)

They stormed off down the Damascus road,
Their weapons ready, a fearful sight!
When, suddenly, they were stopped in their tracks
By an amazing, dazzling, brilliant light.

(They all stop, look up, and cover their eyes dramatically.)

They fell to the ground and covered their eyes.

(Appropriate action)

"What's happening?" cried Saul. "What can it be?"
Then he heard a voice: "Now, tell me, Saul,
Why are you persecuting me?"

(Saul holds his arms up, questioning.)

"Who are you, Lord?" Saul cried out.
"I am Jesus," the voice replied.

Saul was stunned, surprised, amazed!
Had not this Jesus been crucified?

(Ananias enters and takes his seat in a corner of the stage. During the following verse, Saul gets up and acts as though realising he is blind. Two of his men lead him round the stage, eventually to meet Ananias. The others exit.)

When Saul stood up he could not see.
They had to lead him to the town.
Ananias, a Christian, welcomed him there:
"Come in, brother Saul – and please sit down."

(Ananias stands, embraces Saul, and helps him into his seat.)

He placed his hands on Saul's eyes, and said:
"The Lord Jesus has chosen you to be
His friend and servant. Just believe!"
And at that moment, Saul could see!

(Appropriate action)

(During the next verse, the dispersed Christians come onto the stage and greet Saul. His two men exit.)

His eyes were open, he could really see!
Everything at last made sense.
Jesus really was alive!
Why, oh why, had he been so dense?

(Saul taps his head.)

(The Christians, with Ananias, lead Saul across to the other side of the stage, as the imprisoned Christians come up onto the stage to meet them.)

They took him to Jerusalem,
To show the believers their new recruit.
But they all shrank back when they saw him come,
The man who used to persecute.

(Appropriate action)

But Saul soon put their minds at rest.

(Saul gestures appropriately, and the Jerusalem Christians gradually move back towards him.)

"Jesus is alive! It's true!
I met him on the Damascus road,
And now I am a believer too!"

(They all embrace him, shake hands, etc.)

They welcomed him as a brother now.
The change in Saul had been colossal.

(Saul steps forward to centre stage and faces the audience.)

And to prove he was a different man
His name was changed to Paul the Apostle.

(He drops down the letter P on his name badge. Everyone else on stage cheers and claps.)

Follow the Leader

Bible Base
Matthew 21.9, 27.22; John 10.1-18, 20.10-18; Isaiah 53.5-6; Mark
6.34.

Introduction
This piece sets out to illustrate first the characteristics of 'silly
sheep' who will just follow anyone. The idea for the sketch came
from considering the way the crowd switched so quickly from their
cries of "Hosanna!" as the Lord Jesus rode into Jerusalem, to cries
of "Crucify!" a few days later. The sheep start by performing a
number of actions, in unison. Then, when a variant is introduced
by the 'leader-sheep' they copy this in turn. The idea is that the
variant-action is gradually passed down the line until all the sheep
have adopted it. As with any piece of drama involving a group of
performers moving in unison, well-controlled and carefully-
rehearsed movements are essential for its effectiveness. Having
introduced the silly sheep, the sketch then moves to the idea that
there is a Good Shepherd who lays down his life for his sheep.
Sensible sheep, of course, will follow the Good Shepherd.

Cast
About eight 'sheep'
Leader-sheep
Mary (one of the sheep)
Jesus
Caller
Reader

*(The stage is empty. The Caller should be off-stage, if possible
invisible to the audience. The Reader enters to introduce the sketch,
then steps to one side.)*

Reader   We present a short sketch about silly sheep and
                senshible seep . . . shilly sheep and . . . a sort
                shketch about shilly . . . about silly sheep and
                shenshible . . .

*(This can go on as long as you like . . . finally, very deliberately, the
Reader gets it right . . .)*

48

A short sketch about silly sheep and sensible sheep!

(Cheers off-stage)

Caller   Enter!

(The 'sheep' enter in an orderly fashion and stand with their backs to the audience, in a line across the stage. Leader-sheep is one end of the line, Mary the other.)

Caller   Walk!

(The sheep turn to their left and start marching, fairly steadily, on the spot, calling out 'left, left, left, left' in time with their marching. After eight calls of 'left' the Leader-sheep introduces the variant by switching to marching to the right and calling out 'right'. Each sheep in turn looks over their shoulder and switches to the variant, so that this is passed down the line until all of them are marching to the right and calling out 'right'. This should be done so that the calls of 'right' are heard in the gaps between the calls of 'left'. There are four calls of 'right' by the entire group, now facing their right, before . . .)

Caller   Stop!

(The sheep stop and all face the back of the stage again.)

Dance!

(The sheep face the front. A piano starts playing, something fairly corny like the Blue Danube Waltz. The sheep perform a very simple dance routine, lasting, say, four bars of music, and repeat this over and over again. For example, arms folded, bend knees, straighten, turn half left and extend left leg, bend knees, straighten, turn half right and extend right leg. After four of these routines, the Leader-sheep switches to a different routine – this should be something relatively silly! *One at a time the other sheep notice the variant and adopt it themselves. The variant is thus passed down the line one by one until all the sheep have adopted it. After four performances of the variant by all sheep together . . .)*

Caller   Stop!

(The music stops abruptly. The sheep stop dancing and all face the back of the stage again.

The seven times table!

(The sheep face the front and chant the seven times table.)

Sheep   One seven is seven, two sevens are fourteen, three sevens are twenty-one, four sevens are twenty-eight, five sevens are thirty-five, six sevens are forty-two . . .

Leader-sheep Forty-three.

Sheep   Six sevens are forty-two.

Leader-sheep Six sevens are forty-three.

(These last two lines are repeated over and over. After the fourth time, the other sheep one by one drop off from chanting the correct result and join the leader-sheep in chanting the incorrect one. In this way the variant is gradually adopted and passed down the line until all the sheep are chanting 'six sevens are forty-three'. After four of these . . .)

Caller   Stop!

(The sheep stop and all face the back of the stage again.)

We believe!

(The sheep face the front and chant, repeatedly, "We believe in God." This should be done in a ritualised way rather than with conviction, the sheep adopting a pious pose as they chant. There should be a short gap between the chants, to allow space for the variant. After four chants the Leader-sheep switches to making a sheep- bleat, *"Baaa . . . " in the gaps between the chants of 'We believe in God', and starts wandering around the stage aimlessly, imitating a lost sheep. One at a time the other sheep join the leader-sheep, until they are all wandering around the stage bleating!)*

Caller   Stop!

(The sheep stop and all line up facing the back of the stage again.)

Enter Jesus!

(The sheep turn and chant 'Hosanna', waving imaginary palm-branches, as Jesus enters and walks in front of the line of sheep. After four cries of hosanna, the Leader-sheep switches to facing the back of the stage, raising a clenched fist and shouting 'crucify', as Jesus goes round behind the line. One by one, the others switch to this variant. When all are chanting 'crucify', after four times . . .)

Caller   Stop!

(The sheep go down on one knee and remain with their backs to the audience and clenched fists raised. Jesus is revealed behind them, with arms outstretched, with his back to the audience.)

Reader   We all like sheep have gone stray. Each of us turns to their own way. But the Lord made the punishment fall on him.

Jesus   *(Calling out)*
I am the Good Shepherd! I lay down my life for the sheep.

(Jesus snaps into a position as though dying on the cross. He then falls to the ground.)

Caller   Dead!

(The sheep stand, point to Jesus and chant quietly 'Dead, dead, dead, . . . ', as they walk off stage and exit, with the Leader-sheep in the lead. One sheep, Mary, does not follow, but stays standing on the edge of the stage with her head buried in her hands. As the others exit the Reader continues . . .)

Reader   They were like sheep without a shepherd.

(The chant of 'dead' can still be heard off-stage. Jesus stands and steps towards Mary.)

Jesus   Mary.

Mary   *(She turns towards him)*
Alive!
(She looks round excitedly and then runs off to share the good news.)
Alive! Alive! Alive!

(The cries of 'alive' alternate with the off-stage chant of 'dead'. Once Mary is off-stage, there is silence. Jesus faces the audience and holds up his arms in a welcoming gesture, as the Reader continues . . .)

Reader   The Good Shepherd calls his own sheep by name and leads them out. His sheep follow him because they know his voice.

(Blackout)

51

Don't Care, Won't Care, Couldn't Care Less

Bible Base
Genesis 1.1-31, 8.22; Job 28.1-12, 40.15-19; Psalms 8.1-8, 23.1-2, 24.1, 58.1-2, 65.12-13, 95.3-4, 104.18, 121.1; Song of Songs 2.11-13; Amos 5.7,11; Micah 4.3-4; Matthew 5.5; John 3.16; Acts 14.15; Romans 8.19-21; James 5.5; 2 Peter 3.13.

Introduction
This sketch sets out the basis for a Christian response to environmental issues. It starts from the scriptural position that God created a good world and gave human beings responsibility for caring for it. Spoiling our environment does not just have implications for the well-being of humankind both in the present and in the future, but it must also be understood as spoiling God's good creation. John 3.16 tells us that God loved and gave his Son for the world, not just the people in it. The sketch concludes with the Bible's clear implication that God's plan of redemption extends not just to human beings but to the whole of creation. The sketch consists mainly of symbolic representations of human beings' abuse of creation, set in the context of a sequence of verses of scripture, emphasising the word of God's response to the wonders of God's creation. The text for the two Readers is taken entirely from the Bible. The actions of the seven 'Players' should be very carefully choreographed and strongly articulated.

Cast
Readers 1 and 2
Seven Players
Professor (this could be a David Bellamy or David Attenborough impersonation)

(There is a large screen at the back of the stage, covered in large sheets of paper, representing a wall. Imitation brick wallpaper could be used. The seven players run on to the stage, look round furtively, then take out thick marker pens, turn their backs to the audience and scribble on the wall in graffiti style. Each one writes one word of the phrase, "Don't Care, Won't Care, Couldn't Care Less", so that

when they stand back the audience can read the whole phrase. They
then look round furtively again, and scuttle off behind the screen.
The Readers enter and begin . . .)

Reader 1   In the beginning,

Reader 2   God created the heavens and the earth.

Reader 1   And God saw that it was good.

Reader 2   Then God said:

Reader 1   "Let us make human beings in our own image, in
our likeness."

(Two players, one male and one female, emerge from opposite sides
of the screen and walk around the stage, looking in wonder at
everything: each other, things around them, above them, below them,
as suggested by the text that follows.)

Reader 2   So God created human beings in his own image.

Reader 1   Male and female he created them.

(The remaining five players emerge gradually and act similarly.)

Reader 2   God blessed them and said to them,

Reader 1   "Be fruitful and increase in number; fill the earth
and subdue it. Rule over the fish of the sea and the
birds of the air and over every living creature that
moves on the ground."

Players   *(Stopping where they are and speaking as though*
surprised at their God-given responsibility)
We're in charge!
(They now gradually move to form a line across the
front of the stage, with their backs to the audience,
as the reading continues . . .)

Reader 2   Then God said,

Reader 1   "I give you every seed-bearing plant on the face of
the whole earth and every tree that has fruit in it.
They will be yours for food. And to all the beasts
of the the earth and all the birds of the air and all
the creatures that move on the ground –
everything that has the breath of life in it – I give
every green plant for food."

Reader 2   And it was so. God saw all that he had made, and it was very good.

(As the players, now in the line, say the one word each that follows, they turn their heads and shoulders round to address the audience. This should be very slick, with precise, controlled movements.)

Player A   All

Player B   that

Player C   God

Player D   made

Player E   was

Player F   very

Player G   good.

(All except Player E run off to behind the screen.)

Player E   *(Defiantly, emphasising the past tense)*
Was!
(Player E runs off to behind screen also.)

Reader 1   Thus the heavens and the earth were completed in their vast array.

Reader 2   O Lord, our Lord, how majestic is your name in all the earth. You have made us men and women to be rulers over the works of your hands; you put everything under our feet: all flocks and herds and the beasts of the field, the birds of the air, and the fish of the sea.

Players   *(From behind screen, rather more assertively)*
We're in charge!

Reader 1 & 2 *(Together)*
The earth is the Lord's and everything in it, the world, and all who live in it.

Players   *(From behind screen, chanting)*
Don't care, won't care, couldn't care less.

(Professor enters.)

Reader 1   God saw all that he had made, and it was very good.

Professor	*(Out of breath, after climbing)* I'm standing here on this remote mountain-top. It's . . . breath-taking!
Reader 2	I lift up my eyes to the hills.
Reader 1	The Lord is the great God – in his hands are the depths of the earth, and the mountains belong to him.
Professor	And here, in this beautiful, awe-inspiring spot, far away from all human habitation, I have located something most surprising . . .
Reader 2	The high mountains belong to the wild goats; the crags are a refuge for the hyrax.
Professor	Tucked away in this remote, rocky crag, here is a fine example of the ubiquitous, semi-crushed, rusty Coke can.

(He picks up an old Coke can, and holds it as though it were something nasty in his hand, and walks slowly off. The seven players march on briskly from behind the screen, each drinking through a straw from a can of drink.)

Players	*(Rhythmically)* Slurp, slurp, slurp, slurp . . . *(They form a line along the edge of the front of the stage, and, in unison, stop drinking, face the front, hold cans at arms length, crush them, and drop them.)* Wheee! *(They all run off to behind the screen again.)*
Readers 1 & 2	*(Together)* The earth is the Lord's and everything in it, the world, and all who live in it.
Players	*(Chanting in unison from behind the screen)* Don't care, won't care, couldn't care less.
Reader 1	God saw all that he had made, and it . . .
Reader 2	was . . . *(Emphasising the past tense)*

Reader 1   very good.

(Professor enters, gesturing expansively.)

Professor   This desolate area all around me was once a magnificent rain forest, the home of exotic butterflies, falcons and leopards. But now . . .

Reader 1   There is a mine for silver and a place where gold is refined. Iron is taken from the earth, and copper is melted from ore.

(The seven players emerge from behind the screen, in a line, as though tunnelling, whispering in unison, 'Dig, dig, dig, dig, . . .' as the next reading continues. They make their way to the centre of the stage. The Professor raises his hands in despair and exits.)

Reader 2   Man searches the farthest recesses for ore in the blackest darkness. His hand assaults the flinty rock and lays bare the roots of the mountain. He tunnels through the rock; his eyes see all its treasures.

(The players form into a huddle in the centre of the stage, kneeling.)

Players   Five, four, three, two, one, . . .

(Together, they make the sound of a huge explosion and fling themselves back across the stage in all directions. They lie motionless for the next verse.)

Reader 1   But where can wisdom be found? Where does understanding dwell? Man does not realise its worth.

(The players get up and all run off to behind the screen again.)

Readers 1 & 2 *(Together)*
                  The earth is the Lord's and everything in it, the world, and all who live in it.

Players   *(Chanting in unison from behind the screen)*
                  Don't care, won't care, couldn't care less.

Reader 1   God saw all that he had made, and it . . .

Reader 2   was . . .

Reader 1   very good.

(Professor enters, carrying a small white carved object, supposed to be ivory.)

Reader 2   God says,

Reader 1   "Every animal of the forest is mine, and the cattle on a thousand hills. I know every bird in the mountains, and the creatures of the field are mine."

Professor   Twenty years ago, this game reserve in East Africa was teeming with elephants, hundreds of huge tuskers, a magnificent sight. But now, a mere handful. So, "where have all the elephants gone?" I hear you say.

Players   *(From behind screen, singing to tune of 'Where have all the flowers gone')*
Where have all the elephants gone?

Professor   The answer is here in my hand. Ivory. Sixteen tons of elephant were destroyed to make trinkets like this.
(He exits, shaking his head.)

Reader 2   Then the Lord spoke:

Reader 1   "Look at the elephant, which I made along with you and which feeds on grass like an ox."

(The players emerge, as though carrying rifles. They whisper slowly and rhythmically, 'Kill, kill, kill . . .' as the reading continues. They move from one posture to the next, each time aiming their rifles in various directions, with each movement in time with the word 'kill'.)

"What strength he has in his loins, what power in the muscles of his belly! His tail sways like a cedar; his bones are tubes of bronze, his limbs like rods of iron. He ranks first among the works of God."

(The players all point their rifles in the same direction . . .)

Players   Bang!

(There is a scream off-stage, like that of an animal in pain. Then silence for three seconds, while the players hold their positions. They

then rush off stage, as though to get their trophy, chanting quickly in unison . . .)

> Dead, dead, dead, dead . . .
> *(They rush straight back on again – the leader could carry an imitation elephant tusk – to their place behind the screen, chanting . . .)*
> Money, money, money, money . . . .

Readers 1 & 2   *(Together)*
The earth is the Lord's and everything in it, the world, and all who live in it.

Players   *(Chanting in unison from behind the screen)*
Don't care, won't care, couldn't care less.

Reader 1   God saw all that he had made, and it . . .

Reader 2   was . . .

Reader 1   very good.

(Professor enters, gesturing ever more expansively.)

Professor   As you walk through these beautiful green meadows, speckled with cornflowers and marsh marigolds, with sheep drinking from this gentle stream, you feel at peace with the Creator . . .

Reader 1   The Lord is my shepherd, I shall not be in want.

Reader 2   He makes me lie down in green pastures, he leads me beside quiet waters.

Professor   But, tragically, this scene of pastoral tranquillity, is, in fact, the proposed site for the fourth London airport.

(The players emerge immediately, in a formation to suggest a JCB digger – they trundle noisily around the stage, with lots of 'brrrm-brrrm' noises. The Professor tries to carry on speaking . . .)

> This beautiful countryside will be destroyed so that Jumbo jets can carry thousands of package-holiday-makers overseas to spoil other beautiful places with high rise hotels, crass commercialism, noise and . . . aaah!

(The players shove the Professor off-stage, then trundle back to behind the screen.)

Reader 1   The winter is past, the rains are over and gone.

(As the Readers continue, the players, one at a time, like a sequence of aeroplanes coming in to land, zoom noisily across the stage – the Readers react appropriately, flinching, ducking, raising their voices to be heard over the noise, etc . . .)

Reader 2   Flowers appear on the earth; the season of singing has come.

Reader 1   The hills are clothed with gladness.

Reader 2   The meadows are covered with flocks and the valleys are mantled with corn.

(The last player now zooms round the stage and joins the others behind the screen again.)

Readers 1 & 2   *(Together)*
The earth is the Lord's and everything in it, the world, and all who live in it.

Players   *(Chanting in unison from behind the screen)*
Don't care, won't care, couldn't care less.

Reader 1   God saw all that he had made, and it . . .

Reader 2   was . . .

Reader 1   very good.
(Professor enters.)

Reader 2   And God said,

Reader 1   As long as the earth endures, seed time and harvest, cold and heat, day and night will never cease.

Professor   And while we in the European Community once again enjoy bumper harvests and food surpluses, here in the war-torn Horn of Africa, fighting and famine continue to bring suffering and starvation on a massive scale.

(He walks off, as the players emerge from behind the screen, eating from various packets of snacks. They line up along the front of the

stage, as though watching a TV screen, but completely unmoved, as the next verses continue . . .)

Reader 1   In your hearts you devise injustice.

Reader 2   And your hands mete out violence on the earth.

Reader 1   You turn justice into bitterness.

Reader 2   You cast righteousness to the ground.

Reader 1   You trample on the poor.

Reader 2   You have lived on earth in luxury and self-indulgence.

Reader 1   You have fattened yourselves in the day of slaughter.

Players   Don't care, won't care, couldn't care less.

(They screw up their snack packets, discard them and walk off to behind the screen again.)

Reader 2   But the Lord Jesus said,

Reader 1   Blessed are the meek for they will inherit the earth.

(The screen crashes to the ground, and the players all look out in surprise and horror.)

Players   What?

Reader 2   For God so loved the world . . .

Players   Loved the world?

Reader 2   God so loved the world . . .

Player A   Who cares!

Readers 1 & 2 God cares!

Players A   So we should care?

Reader 2   For God so loved the world that he gave his one and only Son.

Players B, C, D *(To each other)*
We should care . . .

Players E, F, G *(To each other)*
We could care . . .

Reader 2	For God so loved the world that he gave . . .
Players	*(Thoughtfully)*
	. . . he gave his one and only Son.

(The players now visibly repent – during the following text they walk slowly towards the front of the stage, where they kneel together in an attitude of prayer.)

Reader 1	And in the last days,
Reader 2	They will beat their swords into ploughshares, and their spears into pruning forks.
Reader 1	Every person will sit under their own vine, and under their own fig-tree, and no-one will make them afraid.
Reader 2	We are looking forward to a new heaven and a new earth, the home of righteousness.
Reader 1	For the creation waits in eager expectation for the sons of God to be revealed.
Reader 2	The creation itself will be liberated from its bondage to decay and brought into the glorious freedom of the children of God.
Players	*(Now kneeling in prayer)*
	Our Father in heaven, forgive us our sins.
Reader 1	So, let us turn from worthless things,
Reader 2	To the living God,
Reader 1	Who made heaven
Reader 2	And earth
Reader 1	And sea
Reader 2	And everything in them.
All	*(Strongly and enthusiastically, with heads raised)*
	Amen!
	(Then quietly and reverently, with heads bowed)
	Amen.

Christian Olympics

Bible Base
1 Corinthians 9.24-26; Philippians 3.13-14; Hebrews 12.1-2; Galatians 5.7; 2 Timothy 2.5; 2 Timothy 4.7-8.

Introduction
The New Testament frequently uses the analogy of running a race to discuss aspects of living the Christian life. I have brought together here most of the verses which employ this analogy and constructed an action-packed seven-lap race. All the incidents in the race are derived from scriptural references, although I have taken the liberty of making some small changes in the actual verses used to fit the actual context of this piece; for example, in places I change 'prize' to 'gold medal'.

The six competitors are: Chris Jacuzzi, who keeps the rules, trains well, runs with his eyes fixed on the finishing line, keeps going with perseverance and eventually wins the gold medal; Betty Bootson, who starts off running in an overcoat and wellies, and who is, not surprisingly, somewhat hindered by them; Amy Aimless, who looks all round her as she runs and eventually runs off in the wrong direction; Maggie Flaggy, who is cut up by another competitor and gives up; Freddy Fiddler, who does the cutting up, crosses the finishing line first, but is disqualified when he fails a drugs test; and Wally Workshy, who doesn't last long due to lack of training! The piece is an excellent discussion starter with a group of young Christians. The analogy is very rich.

Cast
Commentator
Reader
Six Runners: Chris Jacuzzi
Betty Bootson
Amy Aimless
Freddy Fiddler
Maggie Flaggy
Wally Workshy

(The hall must be arranged so that the competitors can run round it and be clearly seen by the audience. The runners start at the front of the hall; then they must go out of sight, e.g. through a door, before reappearing, preferably through another door, in the prescribed order. While they are out of sight there is a reading of the relevant words from the New Testament. This gives the runners the chance to catch their breath, to organise themselves into the right order for their reappearance, and to remind themselves of what must happen on the lap in question! The commentary provided will probably require some extra ad-libbing, in order to keep it going non-stop and to match the actual timing of events in the race. The commentator might be on-stage with the competitors running round the auditorium.)

Commentator Welcome to the 1994 Olympic Games, here in this magnificent stadium in . . . *(insert actual name of venue)*. And we are here today to bring you live coverage of this unique three thousand metres final, featuring both men and women running together, for the first time in an Olympic race. You could say, this is not a men's race, not a women's race, but a human race.

(The six runners emerge and prepare for the race.)

Now here are the six runners coming onto the track. Here they are, magnificent athletes every one of them. Rippling with muscles, finely-tuned bodies. Down there on the track, getting ready now for the race of their lives. Stripping off their track suits. Adjusting their dress. Flexing their muscles, stretching, breathing deeply. You can feel the tension as the seconds tick away.

(The runners line up for the start. Each one greets the audience when their name is called.)

Right, now here's a quick check on the runners. In lane one, we've got Chris Jacuzzi. Good prospect for a gold medal there.
In lane two, there's Betty Bootson – and, if I'm not mistaken, it looks as though she's preparing to run the race wearing an overcoat and wellies! Well, this is unorthodox, to say the least.

In lane three, let's see – ah, yes, that's Amy Aimless – she looks in excellent shape.

And in lane four, there's Freddy Fiddler. Tough competitor, that one. The others will have to keep a close eye on him.

Lane five, that's Maggie Flaggy. She looks pleased to have made it to the final - quite an achievement at her age.

And finally in lane six, there's Wally Workshy. Just look at those legs.

Now, they're getting on their marks. They're ready. And they're off. There they go. Seven laps of the track. The race is on.

(The runners start the race and exit for a short while.)

Reader   The Bible teaches us that living a Christian life is like running in a race. Paul says: "Run in such a way as to get the gold medal."

(The runners reappear . . .)

LAP ONE ORDER OF ENTRY: Maggie, Amy, Wally, Freddy, Betty, Chris.

LAP ONE INCIDENTS: none.

Commentator Now here they come – and let's see, in the lead there is Maggie Flaggy, followed by Amy Aimless – then there's a tight bunch, with Chris Jacuzzi lying last at this stage. There they go. Flaggy, in the lead, Aimless, second, Workshy, lying third. One lap gone. This looks anyone's race at this stage. Six more laps to go to the finishing line.

(The runners exit.)

Reader   "Press on towards the finishing line, to win the gold medal, the prize for which God has called us heavenwards in Christ Jesus."

(The runners reappear . . .)

LAP TWO ORDER OF ENTRY: Wally, Maggie, Amy, Freddy, Betty, Chris.

LAP TWO INCIDENTS: *Wally fades, is overtaken by everyone else and collapses from exhaustion.*

Commentator And as they come round on lap two, well, there's a surprise – Wally Workshy has gone into the lead, but it looks as though he's in trouble. Yes, he's fading fast – and the others are overtaking him. And Wally Workshy has dropped from the race. This is dramatic! End of lap two, there they go off on lap three.

(The runners exit.)

And, would you believe it, Wally Workshy is out of the race. Well, it looks as though the rumours that he has not taken his training seriously might just be true. He's just completely run out of puff.

Reader God's word says: "Everyone who competes in the games goes into strict training. They do it to get a crown which will not last – but we do it to get a crown that will last for ever."

(The runners reappear . . .)

LAP THREE ORDER OF ENTRY: *Amy, Maggie, Freddy, Chris, Betty.*

LAP THREE INCIDENTS: *Betty is well back behind the others, struggling. Amy runs along in the lead, looking all round her; she eventually loses her way and runs off the track. She is then out of the race.*

Commentator Here they come now, on lap three. And there's Amy Aimless taking over the lead, looking very strong. But look at the way she's looking round her as she runs. That's very silly. Maggie Flaggy in second. Third is Freddy Fiddler. Betty Bootson has fallen a long way back. And look at this! Amy Aimless has lost her way and run right off the track and she's out of the race! End of lap three. Only four runners left. Flaggy, Fiddler, Jacuzzi, and bringing up the rear, Bootson.

(The runners exit.)

Reader The Bible says: "Do not run like someone running aimlessly. Let us fix our eyes on Jesus."

LAP FOUR ORDER OF ENTRY: Maggie, Freddy, Chris, Betty.

LAP FOUR INCIDENTS: Betty is clearly struggling. Halfway round she removes her wellies and overcoat, and then gets going well.

Commentator Well, this race is full of drama. We've had one runner dropping out from exhaustion – through lack of training I suspect. And then another losing her way and running off in the wrong direction!

(The runners reappear . . .)

And as the runners come into sight, there's no change at the front, but it looks as though Betty Bootson is really in trouble. That coat and those wellies, they must weigh her down. I don't know how she can possibly run in them. But look at this! She's stopped and she's taking them off! Yes, she's throwing them aside. There they go, wellies, overcoat. Now, she's off again. And she's running like a true athlete. Yes, as they go into lap five, Betty Bootson is back in the race. Come on, Betty! Look at her go.

(The runners exit.)

Reader The Bible says: "Throw off everything that hinders and the sin that so easily entangles, and run with perseverance the race marked out for us."

(The runners reappear . . .)

LAP FIVE ORDER OF ENTRY: Maggie, Freddy, Chris, Betty.

LAP FIVE INCIDENTS: Freddy cuts up Maggie on a bend. This should be in full view of the audience. Maggie gives up.

Commentator Now here they are, coming up towards the end of lap five. Four runners left in it. It's still anyone's race. There's Maggie Flaggy back in the lead, with Freddy Fiddler on her heels, as they go into the bend. And, well, look at that! Fiddler has just cut her up. Right into her path. And he's in front now.

And, look, Flaggy seems to have completely lost heart. Fiddler's cut her up on the bend – and, well, I don't believe it – she's just given up! End of lap five – three runners left.

(The runners exit.)

Reader   Paul wrote to one group of Christians: "Some of you were running a good race. Who cut in on you and kept you from obeying the truth?"

(The runners reappear . . .)

LAP SIX ORDER OF ENTRY: *Freddy, Chris, Betty.*

LAP SIX INCIDENTS: *Betty is back in touch again. It is a close thing between Freddy and Chris for the lead, with Freddy just staying ahead.*

Commentator   They're coming up now approaching the end of lap six. There's Freddy Fiddler in the lead, Chris Jacuzzi is closing on him, with Betty Bootson bringing up the rear. It's Fiddler, Jacuzzi, Bootson. And there they go into the final lap. Fiddler, Jacuzzi, Bootson. What a race between Fiddler and Jacuzzi!

(The runners exit.)

They're all in for medals here, even Bootson now she's recovered from her bad start. That's all in the past now.

Reader   Paul the Apostle says: "I press on to take hold of that for which Christ Jesus took hold of me. Forgetting what is behind, and straining towards what is ahead, I press on towards the finishing line."

(The runners reappear . . .)

LAP SEVEN ORDER OF ENTRY: *Freddy, Chris, Betty.*

LAP SEVEN INCIDENTS: *Freddy and Chris are neck and neck, but Freddy just crosses the line first. Betty comes in third.*

Commentator   And here they come. Last lap. It's Fiddler, then Jacuzzi. Fiddler, Jacuzzi. Bootson's third. Fiddler and Jacuzzi are neck and neck. There's nothing in it. What a race! What a finish! But Fiddler's got it – yes, Fiddler wins. Jacuzzi second. And an honourable third for Bootson. Well, a controversial race that one.

(Freddy does lap of honour.)

Yes, it looks like gold for Freddy Fiddler, but, I must say, there are bound to be questions asked about that incident in lap five, when he cut in on Maggie Flaggy. Jacuzzi ran a good race, but . . . wait a minute, we have some dramatic news, just come in. Results of a drugs test. Fiddler has been disqualified.

(Freddy reacts appropriately and storms off in a fury.)

Freddy Fiddler has tested positive for anabolic steroids, and he is disqualified. He's cheated and he's paid the price. Fiddler loses the gold. He goes home in disgrace. Well, this is high drama.

Reader God's word says: "If anyone competes as an athlete they do not receive the gold medal unless they compete according to the rules."

Commentator So there is the dramatic news from the Olympics here in the . . . *(insert name of actual venue)* stadium. It's gold in the 3000 metres for Chris Jacuzzi. Silver for Betty Bootson.

(Betty congratulates him and he raises his arms in triumph, etc.)

And well deserved too, that win by Jacuzzi. Chris has trained hard for this. He ran a good, clean race. He stuck to the rules. He kept his eyes fixed on the finishing line and kept going with determination right to the end. Jacuzzi takes the gold.
(Encourages the audience to cheer.)

Reader The apostle Paul, near the end of his life, wrote: "I have fought a good fight. I have finished the race. I have kept the faith. Now there is in store for me the crown of righteousness, which the Lord will award to me on that day."

How to be an Alien

Bible Base
Daniel 6.1-28; 1 Peter 2.11-12; Psalm 31.1-15.

Introduction
This is a light-hearted rendering of the story of Daniel being thrown
into the lion's den. Although a Narrator is used to keep the action
moving, there is a certain amount of line-learning for the actors. In
a short play like this it is important that the actors establish their
characters very quickly, exaggerating their attributes. So the King
should be very pompous, and the two administrators should exude
jealousy towards Daniel and unctuousness towards the King, right
from the start. Simple costumes could be used to help identify the
characters as being from Old Testament times. The opening reading
is included to shift the focus away from the lion's den, and more
towards the really important aspects of the story. Daniel, as an
alien in Babylon, had to live an exemplary life and stay faithful to
His God in the midst of a culture which he could only partially
embrace. In this respect he is a good example for all Christians,
since, as Peter points out, we are ourselves, to some extent, "aliens
and strangers in the world."

Cast
Reader
Narrator
Daniel
Administrators A and B
King Darius

*(The stage should be empty except for a seat to represent the King's
throne. Off-stage there should be a screen to represent the lion's den,
so that Daniel and the administrators can be thrown off-stage into
it. King Darius is very full of himself and is easily flattered by the
sycophancy of the two administrators. Appropriate miming is
assumed throughout when the Narrator is speaking. The Reader
enters and stands centre-stage.)*

Narrator Peter, the disciple of Jesus, teaches us that Christians
are like aliens in this present world. In his first letter,

69

he writes: "Dear friends, I urge you, as aliens in the world, to abstain from sinful desires, which war against your soul. Live such good lives among the pagans that, though they accuse you of doing wrong, they may see your good deeds and glorify God."

(Pause)

We present a short play, entitled, "How to be an Alien."

(Exit)

(Enter Darius, gesturing regally. He sits on his throne.)

Narrator *(Off-stage)*

Darius the Mede became king of Babylon. And he appointed 120 satraps to rule over the kingdom, with three administrators over them.

(Enter Daniel, A and B.)

One of these was Daniel, an alien, exiled from the country Israel.

(Daniel waves and points to himself.)

Daniel was the cleverest, most reliable and most hard-working administrator of the three. The king was very pleased with him.

(Darius gets up and pats Daniel on the back, etc.)

Darius   Good man, Daniel.

Narrator He planned to put Daniel in charge of the whole kingdom.

(Darius and Daniel leave the stage together, talking. A and B huddle together, conspiratorially. They deliver their lines with plenty of venom.)

A   Look at that alien, Daniel – always sucking up to the king.

B   Makes you sick, doesn't it!

A   Next thing you know, he'll be in charge of all of us.

B   King's favourite.

A   Yuk!

B   We'll have to do something about this. Quick.

A	Right. I know what! We'll find something wrong what he's done and sneak on him to the king.
B	Yeah – there's bound to be something.
A	A little bribe, a little bit of help-yourself from the treasury purse.
B	A touch of cruelty to his servants. Some error of judgement. A little bit of scandal *(Relishes the word 'scandal')* – we'll get the Sunday papers onto it. See what they can come up with.
A	*(Laughing with menace)* Nothing like a bit of character assassination to stitch up a rival!

(They leave the stage in opposite directions.)

Narrator One week later . . .

(A and B return immediately!)

A	*(Excited)* What have you got? Anything really juicy?
B	*(Disappointed)* Nothing. *(Excited)* What about you?
A	*(Disappointed)* Nothing as well. No-one could find nothing to accuse him of.
B	Of which.
A	Pardon?
B	No-one could find nothing of which to accuse him of. Your grammar's not too good.
A	No, she's been ill for some time.
B	That alien is so flipping trustworthy and reliable. Not a hint of corruption or negligence.

(Daniel returns to the stage and kneels in a corner praying.)

A	You know, the only way we'll ever catch him out is if it's something to do with that God of his.
B	Right. He's always up there in his house praying to his God. OK, listen, this is what we'll do . . .

(They huddle together, whispering. Enter Darius. A and B bow and scrape appropriately.)

A	O King Darius, may you live for ever!
B	You are the greatest king in all the world.
A	Nay, the universe.
B	All people should worship such a great king as you, O great Darius.
Darius	True. Yes, very true. I am indeed a great king. Please carry on.
A	You should pass a law, O king. That for the next thirty days anyone who worships any god or any man other than you, O great King Darius, should be . . . um . . . should be . . .
B	Thrown into the lion's den!
A	Yes, thrown into the lion's den.
Darius	Yes, that seems very reasonable to me. Right, I issue this edict: Anyone who worships any . . .
A	Put it in writing, your majesty.
B	Then according to the laws of the Medes and Persians it cannot be altered, O great King Darius.
Darius	OK, if you say so. O blow, I haven't got anything to write on.
A	*(Handing him a scroll)* You are desirous of papyrus, King Da-*ri*-us?
Darius	Oh, thanks. Oh dear, now I haven't got anything to write with.
B	*(Handing him a pencil)* An essential utensil, a pencil, O great and mighty King Darius.

(Darius writes, while A acts as though dictating to him.)

Narrator And so the king put the decree into writing. Now anyone who for the next thirty days prayed to any god or any man would be thrown . . .

Narrator, A and B
. . . into the lion's den!

(A takes the decree. A and B exit, stage left, chuckling, looking in Daniel's direction. Darius exits stage right. Daniel gets up and walks around the stage, looking anxious.)

Narrator When Daniel heard about the king's decree, he went home to his upstairs room, where the windows opened towards Jerusalem.

(Daniel returns to the corner where he prays.)

Three times a day he got down onto his knees and prayed, just as he had done before.

(A and B walk past the front of the stage and spot Daniel as he is praying. They point at him, whisper together and run off excitedly.)

Daniel *(Praying)*
In you, O Lord, I have taken refuge. Let me never be put to shame. Deliver me in your righteousness. Into your hands I commit my spirit. They conspire against me and plot to take my life. But I trust in you, O Lord. I say, "You are my God." My times are in your hands.
(He gets up and exits.)

(Enter Darius stage right. A and B enter stage left and rush up to him. They bow and scrape and speak very quickly.)

A O King Darius, may you live for ever, et cetera, et cetera . . .

B You are the greatest king in all the world, blah, blah, blah . . .

A You know that decree what you wrote.

Darius Pardon?

A *(Waving the scroll)*
Remember?

Darius Ah yes. The decree. You can't change it now, you know. In accordance with the laws of the Medes and the Persians, it cannot be altered.

A Quite.

B Precisely.

(A and B continue with extreme unctuousness.)

A Well, you know that Daniel.

B The alien. From Jerusalem.

Darius But of course. He's a good man, Daniel. I was thinking of . . .

A Well, he pays no attention to your decree, O great and mighty king Darius.

B He still prays three times a day, O most worthy royal personage. He prays to his God!

A So, O great and mighty King Darius – may you live for ever – what must we do with him?

Darius *(Horrified)*
What? You mean? But he's a good man, Daniel.

B According to your decree . . .

Darius What? Throw him . . . into . . .

A and B Yes?

Darius Into . . .

A and B Yes?

Darius Into . . . the lion's den!

A and B Yes!

(A and B jump up and down exit excitedly. Darius acts distressed.)

Darius But he's a good man, Daniel!

Narrator And King Darius was greatly distressed.

Darius I am greatly distressed!

(Exit A and B. Darius flops into his seat, holding his head.)

Narrator And King Darius made every effort to save Daniel, but, according to the laws of the Medes and the Persians, the decree could not be altered.

(A and B return, escorting Daniel.)

A Come on, Daniel. This way.

B Dinner time. Puss, puss, puss . . .

(The King waves them on and turns his head away.)

Narrator The king gave the order and they brought Daniel and threw him . . .

Narrator, A and B
Into the lion's den!

(A and B throw Daniel off-stage, into the lion's den, and rub their hands with glee.)

Darius *(Standing up and calling out to Daniel)*
May your God – the one whom you serve day and night – may he have mercy on you, Daniel!

Narrator They closed the lion's den and the king sealed it with his own signet ring.

(Appropriate action)

(A and B exit. Darius mimes following action.)

The king returned to his palace. That evening he was thoroughly miserable.

Darius I am thoroughly miserable!

Narrator There, I told you he was thoroughly miserable.

(Darius lies on the floor and acts appropriately.)

Narrator All night he tossed and turned in his bed. He could not sleep a wink.

Darius *(Crying out)*
But, he's a good man, Daniel!

Narrator Dawn broke.

(There is a crash off-stage.)

Darius got up and hurried to the lion's den.

(Darius rushes over to the edge of the stage and calls out . . .)

Darius Daniel, Daniel! Servant of the living God. Has your God been able to rescue you from the lion's den?

(Silence)

Daniel? Daniel! Oh woe is me!

Daniel *(Popping his head out from behind the screen)*
Surprise! O king, may you live for ever. My God did indeed send his angel to rescue me, to shut the mouths of the lions.

Darius What? How? Why?

Daniel Because I am innocent in his sight and I have never done any wrong before you, O King.

Darius There, I said you were a good man, Daniel!

Narrator And the king was overjoyed.

Darius I am overjoyed!
(He does a little jig of delight.)
It's a miracle!
(Calling to A and B)
Come quickly, you men – bring Daniel from the lion's den.

(A and B run on, are amazed to see Daniel alive, bring him up onto the stage . . . and then appropriate action as follows:)

And now you two – you who tricked me with your clever scheme – there's only one place for you.

A and B No!

Darius Yes!

A and B No!

Darius Yes! The lion's den!

(Daniel escorts A and B to the edge of the stage, they leap off, behind the screen, screaming – then silence.)

Darius *(Looking into the den, and acting appropriately)*
Ooh, nasty!

Narrator Then King Darius wrote a new decree.

Darius This is a new decree what I wrote.
(Clears throat and reads from a scroll)

76

"In every part of my kingdom, people must fear and reverence the God of Daniel. For he is the living God and he endures for ever. His kingdom will not be destroyed. His dominion will never end. For he has rescued Daniel from the power of the lions." Praised be the God of Daniel!

(Daniel and Darius exit.)

Reader *(Taking centre stage, as Daniel and Darius walk off together)*
"Dear friends, I urge you, as aliens in this world, to live such good lives among the pagans that, though they accuse you of doing wrong, they may see your good deeds and glorify God."

HERE IS THE NEWS

General Introduction

The following four sketches, coming under the general heading of *Here is the News*, show how a simple, basic framework can be used to re-tell any Bible story in a lively and humorous way. They could be used with an audience of children or, for example, at a Family Service.

A mock television news studio is used as a device for communicating the essence of the Bible story being considered. Interplay between the characters in the news team, plus on-the-spot interviews with characters from the Bible story, allow for both humour and pace in the presentation.

The stage should be set up with as much appropriate equipment as possible: such as lights, cameras and microphones. The newscaster sits at an appropriate table to read the news. The director and the reporters can, quite naturally, carry clip-boards, with scripts on, so there is no need for a great deal of learning of lines.

The following constitute the news team, most of whom appear in most of the sketches:

Dave	*the Director*
Trevor Cheeseburger	*the Newscaster*
Kate Grady and	
Daley Bulletin	*Reporters*
Julie-Darling	*Continuity and make-up*

Dave, the director, wanders around in front of the stage, with headphones on, keeping the action moving. He is slightly precious, calling everyone 'love ' and 'darling'. He wears a flowery shirt and jeans. Trevor Cheeseburger, the newscaster, delivers the news to a microphone, seated at a table. He should wear a jacket and bow-tie. The two reporters are suitably earnest, delivering their reports breathlessly and with much excitement. They should be sited on a corner of the stage, with a hand-mike for interviewing various characters. They could wear something like khaki jackets.

The four stories dealt with here are linked by the common theme of 'news'. We actually used them as starting points during a Holiday Club on the theme of *Good News, Bad News*. Each day the children followed up the drama by working in groups as newspaper reporters, producing their own newspaper account of the Bible story in question. (Following the drama, we arranged each day for one of the main Bible characters in the story to be available for a press conference.)

The first three reports are done in a style which should appeal to an audience of children, with a fair sprinkling of corny jokes. The first report is about King David receiving good news and bad news from the battle in the forest of Ephraim. This may seem an unusual choice of Bible story to dramatise for children, but we felt that the story was full of the kind of exciting action which lends itself to a newspaper report. The second report is the story of Jonah being sent to take bad news to Nineveh, and his reluctance to do it. The third news bulletin recounts the uproar in the synagogue when Jesus announced that he was the one sent to bring good news to the poor.

The fourth news report is necessarily more serious in tone than the others, dealing with the sad news of Jesus's death and leading to the amazing news of his resurrection.

HERE IS THE NEWS
1. Good News and Bad News

Bible Base
2 Samuel 18

Introduction
(See general introduction for *Here is the News*.)
This news report deals with an exciting, but poignant story from the life of King David. His rebellious son, Absalom, has raised an army to try to defeat David and take over the throne. In spite of everything, though, David goes on loving Absalom and does not want him harmed. The messengers from the front-line have to bring the king both good news and bad news. The good news is that the rebel army has been defeated; the bad news that Absalom is dead. This story provides a parallel illustration to the story of the prodigal son: just as David went on loving Absalom in spite of his rebelliousness, God goes on loving us, even when we turn against him, and he wants us to return to him. We have used this story to introduce the idea that the Bible has both bad news and good news for all of us, just like the messengers had bad news and good news for King David. The bad news is that all of us have disobeyed God's laws and fall far short of his holy standards. The good news is that God loves us and sent his Son, Jesus, to be our Saviour and to bring us back to him.

Cast
Dave the Director
Trevor Cheeseburger
Professor Brainy Bonce
Kate Grady
Daley Bulletin
Julie-Darling
Joab
Weather Forecaster (optional)

(NB King David does not actually appear in this sketch. This is so that he can appear later for a press conference, if using the follow-up

80

idea of getting groups of children to produce their own newspaper reports, as suggested in the introduction.)

(Dave enters and calls everyone into action. The speech provided below can be supplemented with as much ad-libbing as necessary. There is immediately lots of business. Trevor enters, putting on his jacket and his bow-tie. Julie-Darling fusses about, moving equipment, dealing with Trevor's make-up, adjusting his bow-tie, combing his hair, etc. Scripts are passed around, furniture moved, mikes adjusted, etc. – all in a frantic hurry to be ready on time . . .)

Dave Right, everyone, two minutes to go. Come on, luvvies, in your places for the main news. Bottoms on seats, please, quick as poss. Cameras ready? Lovely. Check make-up please, Julie-Darling. OK? Here we go. One minute everyone. Everything OK, Trevor-luv? Julie-Darling, put his bow-tie straight. Got your script, Trevor?

Trevor Got it, Dave. So, what's today's main story?

Dave We've got reports coming in of a major battle in Israel. Bit messy, but we'll run with it. We've got our top reporters on the spot and you've got Professor Brainy Bonce for expert commentary.

(Professor enters, shakes Trevor's hand and takes a seat next to him. The Professor is brought in later to provide important background to the events. He is, of course, rather absent-minded and doesn't always hear what is being said to him.)

All set to blow their minds with lots of clever facts, professor-luv? OK, twenty seconds now. Lots of hush in the studio. Here we go . . . ten, nine, eight, seven, six, five, four, three, two, one . . .

(The audience can be encouraged to join in the countdown.)

Cue intro.

Julie-Darling And now here on Channel Five and a Half, it's time once again for News at Five Past Six, presented by Trevor Cheeseburger.

Dave Cue music.

(There is a brief snatch of music.)

Dave	Right, off you go, Trevor-luv.
Trevor	Good evening, and welcome to News at Five Past Six. And our main story today is of a fierce battle raging in Israel. News is coming in that King David has retreated from Jerusalem with his army and crossed the river Jordan, hotly pursued by the King's son, Absalom, with his huge band of rebel forces. We're going over now to our reporter on the spot, Kate Grady.
Dave	Cue Kate.
Trevor	Kate Grady, can you hear me?
Kate	Hello, Trevor. Yes, I can hear you.
Trevor	Kate?
Kate	Trevor?
Dave	Get on with it!
Trevor	Kate, can you tell us exactly where are the king's armies?
Kate	Well, Trevor, the King's armies are in his sleevies.
Trevor	I mean, what is the situation at the battle-front?
Kate	There's a fierce battle going on here in the forest of Ephraim. The troops loyal to the king are outnumbered by the rebels, but they are fighting with tremendous courage. The area all round me is littered with casualties. Some estimates are that there might be as many as twenty thousand killed.
Trevor	And is there any news of King David?
Kate	Well, I've been talking to some of the troops. They say that the king wanted to lead them into battle, but they persuaded him that he should stay back at their base in the city of Mahanaim. They told him he would be no use to them dead.
Trevor	And what about the king's son, Absalom?
Kate	I understand that he's here somewhere in the thick of the battle – but where in this forest he might be

is anyone's guess. It's chaos. As I stand here, there are arrows flying all round me,

(All available hands, off-stage, should throw paper arrows at Kate)

men charging in all directions with swords at the ready, soldiers on foot, soldiers on horses and mules. It's absolute mayhem here. I must take cover. Quickly. Ouch!
(She rubs her bottom, as if hit by an arrow.)
This is Kate Grady, in the forest of Ephraim, with a sore bottom, handing you back to Trevor Cheeseburger in the studio.

Dave   Go to interview, Trevor-luv.

Trevor   Now, here in the studio, we have an expert in Middle-Eastern affairs, from . . . *(insert name of locality)* University, Professor Brainy Bonce.

Dave   Camera one on Professor.

Trevor   Professor Brainy Bonce, can you remind us what this war is all about?

Professor   What's that, young man? Who are you anyway?

Trevor   I said:
(Shouting)
Professor Brainy Bonce . . .

Professor   That's odd, that's my name as well.

Trevor   No, my name is Trevor . . .
(Under his breath)
Silly old fool.

Professor   Trevor Silly-old-fool? That's an unusual name.

Trevor   No, Trevor Cheeseburger.

Professor   Pardon?

Trevor   *(Shouting)*
Cheeseburger!

Professor   Oh, no thank you, I've just had my tea. Now what is it you wanted to know?

Trevor	Professor, can you remind us what this war is all about?
Professor	What war?
Trevor	This war in Israel between King David and his son Absalom.
Professor	Oh that war! Yes, very sad. Father and son, just can't seem to get on together. Such a handsome fellow, too, that Absalom.
Trevor	So, all this fighting and bloodshed, it's all about a family squabble?
Professor	More or less. Absalom had been sent into exile by the king for about five years, because he had an argument with one of his brothers and arranged to have him 'bumped off', so to speak. When his old man allowed him back into Jerusalem, Absalom started to plot to take over the throne.
Trevor	Did the king hear about this?
Professor	Yes – which is why he got all his men together and escaped off to the north. Away from Jerusalem, David can organise his attack on the rebel forces.
Trevor	I suppose King David won't be satisfied until Absalom is safely in his grave?
Professor	On the contrary. He still loves his son, in spite of everything. In fact, I've heard that he told his troops that Absalom had to be protected.
Trevor	So would you say that King David wants to defeat the rebels, but save his son, at the same time?
Professor	Time? *(Looking at his watch)* Just gone quarter past ten. But I might be a bit slow.
Trevor	Yes, you could say that.
Professor	No, I would say that King David wants to defeat the rebels, but save his son, at the same time.

Dave	Cut the interview, Trevor-luv, news flash from the front. Go over to Kate now.
Trevor	Professor Brainy Bonce, thank you very much.
Professor	Thank you, Mr Hamburger.
Trevor	Cheeseburger!
Professor	Oh, no thanks, I'll just get myself a sandwich.

(Professor exits.)

Trevor	Now we go across to Kate Grady in the forest of Ephraim, for a news flash. Kate.
Kate	Trevor.
Trevor	Kate.
Kate	Well, Trevor, it looks as though the battle is over. The rebel forces have been defeated. I'm standing here under a large oak tree. Just above me, hanging in the branches of the tree is the body of Absalom. The King's son is dead.
Trevor	So, Absalom's plans have come to nothing. He set out to defeat the king's army, only to die?
Kate	No, Trevor. He set out to defeat the king's army only yester-die. Now, I have here one of the leaders of the king's army, Commander Joab.

(Joab enters and is interviewed by Kate. He delivers his lines in a clipped military-style voice, with lots of hand gestures.)

Kate	Commander Joab, what happened?
Joab	Tree here. We were over there. Absalom coming from over there. Riding mule. Must have come very fast. From there. To here. Hit this branch here. Head caught there. Mule carried on over there. Absalom stuck in tree here. We came from over there to over here. Saw enemy hanging here. Took three javelins here. One, two, three. All over. End of story. Enemy dead, here. Victory for King David.
Kate	So, has King David heard the news?

Joab	Not yet. Sent messengers. Right away. From here. To there. On their way now. Good news, bad news. For the king. Must go. Messy business . . .
Kate	Thank you, Commander Joab. This is Kate Grady, with good news and bad news for King David, handing you back to the studio.

(They both exit. Daley Bulletin takes his place.)

Dave	News flash coming in from Mahanaim, Trevor.
Trevor	Thank you, Kate Grady. Now we have another news flash, direct from the king's camp. We go over to our reporter on the spot, Daley Bulletin. Live from Mahanaim, across the River Jordan. Daley.
Daley	Trevor.
Trevor	Are you reporting from the king's camp, Daley?
Daley	No, I am reporting from the king's camp about once a week.
Trevor	So, what is happening now?
Daley	Well, Trevor, there's been tremendous confusion here in the king's camp. First a young man called Ahimaaz brought the good news that the rebel armies had been defeated. But he had no news for the king of what had happened to Absalom. It seemed that the king was more concerned about his son than the result of the battle. Then a second messenger arrived.
Trevor	And what was the message that he brought?
Daley	I have here a copy of the statement he made to the king. It reads: "My lord, the king, hear the good news! The Lord has delivered you today from all who rose up against you."
Trevor	But still no news of Absalom?
Daley	Well, the king then pressed him for news of his son and the messenger had to admit that he had bad news as well. Absalom was dead. The king is

	heart-broken. The victory celebrations have been turned into a day of mourning.
Dave	Cut back to studio. Twenty seconds to go to the weather forecast. Trevor . . .
Trevor	So there we have it. Good news and bad news for King David. Good news that the rebel army is defeated and he may now return to his throne in Jerusalem. But also bad news, that Absalom, the son he loved so much in spite of everything, is dead. And that is the end of the news.

* **(The following ending might not be suitable in all circumstances, so an alternative is provided below.)**

Trevor	Now, we go across to the . . . (*insert name of locality*) Weather Centre for the weather forecast. What have you got for us this evening? Good news or bad news on the weather front?
Weather Forecaster	
	Bad news, I'm afraid, Trevor. We could get really wet this evening. There are heavy showers expected in the . . . *(insert name of locality)* area. Any minute . . . now!

(During this speech, Julie-Darling creeps up behind Trevor with a bucket of water, and, coinciding with the word 'now', she throws it all over him!)

* **(Alternative ending . . . everyone except Trevor leaves the stage.)**

Trevor	So, that's the news this evening. Join us again tomorrow for News at Five Past Six. In the meantime, stay tuned to Channel Five and a Half, the channel that brings you good news as well as bad. This is Trevor Cheeseburger, saying good night from me, and . . .
	(Looking around)
	. . . good night from me.

HERE IS THE NEWS
2. Overseas and Underseas News

Bible Base
Jonah 1-3

Introduction
(See general introduction for *Here is the News.*)
This Channel Five and a Half news report deals with the story of Jonah. The main focus is on the fact that Jonah was running away from God because he did not want to have to take bad news to Nineveh: the news of God's judgement on their sin. However, once he had delivered the message as required, the people did repent and turn back to God. God's messengers today, likewise, do not enjoy having to tell people the 'bad news' of God's judgement upon our sin. But until we understand this, we cannot appreciate the good news of his forgiveness through Jesus Christ, and then respond to him in repentance and faith.

Cast
Dave the Director
Trevor Cheeseburger
Kate Grady
Daley Bulletin
Julie-Darling
Captain Fishfinger
Weather Forecaster (optional)

(NB Jonah does not actually appear in this sketch. This is so that he can appear later for a press conference, if using the follow-up idea of children producing their own newspaper accounts of the story, as suggested in the introduction.)

(Dave enters and calls everyone into action. As in the previous sketch, Dave's opening speeches provided below can be supplemented with as much ad-libbing as necessary. There is immediately lots of business, with everyone trying to get the studio ready in time for the news report . . .)

Dave	Right, everyone, two minutes to go for today's news broadcast. Come on, luvvies, get your pretty little selves organised now. This studio looks a shambles. Make-up, do something about Trevor, there's a sweetie. Quick as poss. This is television, you know. Lovely. OK everyone, bottoms on seats. One minute to take off.
Trevor	What's the top story today then? Another juicy battle?
Dave	No, nothing as nasty as that. Human interest story today, Trevor-luv. Lots of pathos. Script, please, for Trevor. Thank you, sweetie. Lots of hush, please. Right, we're counting. Ten seconds, nine, eight, seven, six, five, four, three, two, one . . . *(Encourages the audience to join in the countdown.)* Cue intro.
Julie-Darling	And now here on Channel Five and a Half it's time once again for News at Five Past Six, presented by Trevor Cheeseburger.
Dave	Cue music.
(Music)	
	Sock it to them, Trevor-luv.
Trevor	Good evening, and welcome to News at Five Past Six. And our main story today is an extraordinary tale of a man swallowed by a sea monster. Here's Kato Grady reporting from Joppa.
Kate	Following a severe storm at sea, early today a man was found lying exhausted on the beach nearby to this city. His story is that he was swallowed by some kind of monster fish.
Trevor	Kate, how did he come to be in this place?
Kate	No, it wasn't a plaice, Trevor. Much bigger than a plaice. More like a whale. Quite a whopper, actually.
Trevor	Where did he come a cropper in this whopper.

Kate	Near to Joppa.
Trevor	Tell us how he got onto the beach.
Kate	Well, Trevor, the man's name is Jonah. Apparently he had been on board a ship heading for Tarshish. The captain of the ship is here with me now. Captain Fishfinger . . .

(Enter the Captain, to be interviewed by Kate. He is dressed in a fisherman's cape and hat. His speech is interspersed with lots of oohs, aahs and ayes and other strange noises. He splutters as he speaks, so that Kate has occasionally to take out a handkerchief to dry her face!)

Captain	Ooh, aah, aye, aye, aah . . . (*etc.*)
Kate	Captain Fishfinger, what can you tell us about this man Jonah?
Captain	Ooh, aah, aye, 'e was a-running away, yer see. From 'is God. On account of the message 'e 'ad to take to the city of Nineveh.
Kate	Message from God? Was that good news or bad news?
Captain	Ooh, aah, bad news that be. Very bad news. Terrible bad news. Jonah, 'e say that 'is God 'ad seen 'ow wicked and disobedient were the people of Nineveh. And 'e be right angry with 'em. Aah, that be bad news for Nineveh.
Kate	So why was Jonah running away, Captain?
Captain	Aah, well, 'e don't like to take 'em the bad news, do 'e now? So 'e gets on my ship, going to Tarshish. And we 'ave this terrible storm. A great and mighty wind. Fearful strong it be. And these violent waves come crashing into our 'umble little ship. We was scared out of our skins. Aah, aye, it were right dreadful. In all my years at sea I never see nowt like it. I feared the ship were a-going under.
Kate	So did you throw the cargo overboard?

90

Captain	Aye, that we did. To try to save 'er. But it were no good. Someone were bringing us bad luck, we reckon. So, we drew lots and this 'ere Jonah 'e draws the short straw.
Kate	So, what did you do?
Captain	Ooh, aah. We asked 'im, yer see. And 'e says it was all 'appening because it be 'is fault for running away from 'is God and not taking the bad news to Nineveh. And 'e tell us to chuck 'im overboard.
Kate	So, did you "chuck 'im overboard"?
Captain	Ooh, aah, aye. But not at first. Yer see, 'e were an 'armless old bloke, and we didn't like to do it. So we tried to row to land, but the storm it were so fierce, and the wind, ooh, the wind. Ooh, we did suffer from the wind! The sea it were wild and violent, the waves were crashing over the side. So we chucked 'im overboard. Wheee . . .
Kate	And then?
Captain	Splash!
Kate	And then?
Captain	Gurgle, gurgle.
Kate	And then?
Captain	Then the sea became calm. Aye, ah, just like a mill pond it be.
Kate	Thank you, Captain.
Trevor	Kate, have you spoken to Jonah about what happened then?
Kate	Yes, Trevor, I have. Apparently, as he was sinking beneath the waves, thinking his end had come, this huge fish appeared and swallowed him alive. Somehow he managed to survive inside the fish for three days and nights. During this time he was able to pray to God and realised he must complete the task that God had given him.

Trevor	To go to Nineveh to tell them of God's anger with their wickedness?
Kate	That's it. Well, this morning the fish vomited Jonah up out of its belly and deposited him on the beach. *(Beginning to feel sick herself, talking about it.)*
Captain	Shplat! *(Or some appropriate sound effect)*

(This makes Kate feel really ill. She reacts appropriately.)

Trevor	Charming.
Kate	This is Kate Grady, on the beach at Tarshish, feeling sick, returning you to the studio.

(She rushes off. Exit Captain. Enter Daley.)

Dave	News flash coming in from Nineveh, Trevor. Go over quickly to Daley.
Trevor	Now we go over to our reporter, Daley Bulletin, in Nineveh, for a news flash. Are you there, Daley?
Daley	No, I'm only here about once a year.
Trevor	Daley, what's happening there in Nineveh?
Daley	I am standing here in the centre of this vast city. A great commotion has been caused here by the arrival of a prophet by the name of Jonah. Standing in the centre of the city, he called the leaders together and denounced all the wickedness of their city.
Trevor	What kinds of things did he raise with them, Daley?
Daley	He spoke of their greed and their cruelty, their pride, their refusal to acknowledge the one true God. He told them to stop worshipping idols, to be fair to one another, to be honest, and to cut out sexual immorality. And he warned them that because of their wickedness God would send destruction on the city within forty days.

Trevor	And what has been the effect of this bad news on the citizens of Nineveh?
Daley	Quite remarkable. They appear to have accepted the message as the word of God for them. There has been an amazing atmosphere of repentance. People seem to be really sorry for the way they have been living their lives. Everywhere you look people are turning to God to seek his forgiveness.
Trevor	What about the king?
Daley	Yes, even the king of Nineveh has joined in. He has appeared this afternoon, sitting in the dust of the city square, without his royal robes, dressed only in sack-cloth, and praying for God to have mercy on him and his city.
Dave	Right, wind it up, Trevor. Go to weather forecast.
Trevor	Well, remarkable news there from Nineveh. We will await further developments. And we can assure you that for the next forty days, we at News at Five Past Six will have our cameras on the spot ready to bring you film of the destruction of the city, as soon as it happens. And that is the end of the news.

* (The following ending might not be suitable in all circumstances, so an alternative is provided below.)

Trevor	Now, we go across to the . . . (*insert name of locality*) Weather Centre to see what's in store for us today on the weather front. (*Trevor gets an umbrella ready.*) So, is it good news or bad news?
Weather Forecaster	
	Well, Trevor, it looks as though it's going to be good news. It should be fairly bright later on, with lots of sunshine and a lovely, clear evening in prospect.
Trevor	Phew, that's a relief. (*Puts umbrella away.*)

Weather Forecaster
But not until we've had some heavy showers in the early part of the evening.

(During this speech, Julie-Darling has crept up behind Trevor with a bucket of water, which she now throws all over him)

* (Alternative ending)

Trevor   So, that's all the news for this evening. Join us again tomorrow for News at Five Past Six. In the meantime, stay tuned to Channel Five and a Half, the channel that brings you good news as well as bad. This is Trevor Cheeseburger, saying . . .

Dave   Say good night, Trevor.

Trevor   Good night Trevor.

HERE IS THE NEWS
3. Riot in Nazareth

Bible Base
Luke 4.14-30

Introduction
(See general introduction for *Here is the News*.)
This Channel Five and a Half news report presents the story of the uproar caused by Jesus in the synagogue when he returned to his home town of Nazareth. The commotion seems to have been caused by the carpenter's son claiming that he himself was the fulfilment of Isaiah's prophecy that God would send his anointed one with good news for the poor.

Cast
Dave the Director
Trevor Cheeseburger
Kate Grady
Daley Bulletin
Sarah – a woman from Nazareth
Scribe
Julie-Darling

(NB If using the follow-up idea of getting groups of children to produce their own newspaper accounts, as suggested in the introduction, Mary, the mother of Jesus, who was presumably around in Nazareth when this incident occurred, could appear after this sketch for a press conference.)

(Dave enters and calls everyone into action. As in the previous two sketches the opening speech provided below should be supplemented with as much ad-libbing as necessary. As before, there is immediately lots of business, with everyone concerned rushing round trying to get the studio ready in time for the news report . . .)

Dave   Right, everyone, two minutes to go. Come on, luvvies. In your places for the main news. Bottoms on seats, please, quick as poss. Check make-up please, Julie-darling. Get Trevor's bow-tie straight. OK? Here we go. One minute everyone. Do something about Trevor's hair, please, Julie-darling. Cameras ready? Lovely. Lights, please. Everything OK, Trevor-luv? Got your script? Lovely. Lots of hush in the studio. Right, 20 seconds now, here we go . . . ten, nine, eight, seven, six, five, four, three, two, one, cue intro.

Julie-Darling And now here on Channel Five and a Half, it's time once again for News at Five past Six, presented by Trevor Cheeseburger.

Dave Cue music.

(Music)

Right, Trevor, off you go . . . now!

Trevor Good evening, and welcome to News at Five Past Six. First the headlines.

(Bong)

Unofficial sources in Samaria report that a woman has fallen into a well. Police are looking into it.

(Bong)

In Jerusalem a large flock of doves has escaped from the Temple courts. Officials have called in the flying squad to look for them.

(Bong)

A giraffe and a mouse have been stolen from Bethlehem zoo. Police are hunting high and low.

(Bong)

And reports are coming in of a riot going on at this very moment in a synagogue in Nazareth. We start with that story from Nazareth. In recent months, news of the man known as Jesus of Nazareth has been spreading all round our region. Crowds have been following him everywhere to hear his teaching. There have been well-confirmed reports of a number of cases of miraculous healing. But today the story of this remarkable man has taken an unexpected twist. Returning to his home town of Nazareth for the first time for a number of years, he seems to have sparked off a small riot.

Dave   Go over to Kate, Trevor-luv.

Trevor   We go over now to our reporter on the spot in Nazareth, Kate Grady. Kate, can you hear me?

Kate   Hello, Trevor. Yes, I can hear you, loud and clear.

Trevor   Kate, you are on the spot there in Nazareth, can you describe for us the position at this moment?

Kate   Well, Trevor, at this moment, I am leaning forward, with my legs slightly apart, holding the microphone in my right hand and the script in my left.

Trevor   No, I mean what is the situation with this riot? Is Nazareth still a-buzz?

Kate   No, Trevor. Nazareth never has been a bus, it's a town. However there is still quite a commotion here, following an incident a little while ago in the local synagogue, when the teacher, Jesus, arrived.

Trevor   Was the congregation very large?

Kate   Several of them were fairly large, Trevor. Especially some of the women. Well, the synagogue was absolutely packed. Just what you would expect for a local boy becoming famous and returning home

Trevor   Presumably, on such an occasion as this, Jesus would have been invited to read the lesson in the service.

Kate   That's right. The minister handed him the scroll and he unrolled it reverently and found the set reading for the day. All eyes were fixed upon him as he began to read.

Trevor   So, would you say, they were all agog in the synagogue?

Kate   No, Trevor, I would try to avoid saying that.

Dave	Move to interview with woman, Kate.

(Sarah, in typical Biblical costume, enters, to be interviewed by Kate.)

Kate	Now, I actually have here a woman called Sarah, who is actually from Nazareth and who was actually there in the synagogue. Sarah, do you actually recall what it was that Jesus actually read? Actually?
Sarah	Yes, it was a passage from Isaiah, speaking of the promised Messiah. I know those words so well – we often read them at home and pray for the day when God will send the chosen one with good news for poor people like us. "The Spirit of the Lord is upon me, because he has anointed me to preach good news to the poor . . . he has sent me to announce that now is the time of God's grace." He read it so beautifully.
Kate	Then what happened?
Sarah	He handed the scroll back to the minister, turned and looked at us. And then . . . , well . . .
Kate	Yes?
Sarah	Then he said, "Today these words of prophecy have come true in your hearing." Well! For a moment there was stunned silence, and then suddenly there was an uproar. I mean, we all know who he is, this Jesus – he's Joseph's son, the carpenter. Why, his mother Mary lives just round the corner from me, with his brothers and sisters. How could he stand up in our synagogue like that and start claiming that he was the one God was going to send to save us!
Dave	OK Kate, cut the interview, we've got a scribe lined up for you.
Kate	Thank you, Sarah. Trevor.
Trevor	Kate.
Kate	Trevor?

Trevor	Kate, have you managed to get hold any of the scribes?

(Sarah exits and is replaced by Scribe, also in appropriate costume.)

Kate	Well, no, but one of them is here to talk to me. Sir, I believe you have been actually involved in the actual riot. What made you all so angry?
Scribe	*(Remembering what Jesus had said . . .)* "The Spirit of the Lord is upon me . . . he has anointed me . . . to preach good news to the poor . . . this day this prophecy is coming true in your hearing!" We can't just sit and take that from one of our own local lads. Huh! Then he makes things worse . . .
Kate	How is that?
Scribe	He turns on us and says, "So the old proverb is true, eh? A prophet is honoured everywhere except in his own town." Then – would you believe it – he goes on to tell us that if we won't listen to him, then God's blessing would be taken elsewhere, even to the Gentiles!
Kate	So, tell us, how do you feel?
Scribe	I thought you'd never ask. *(Getting more and more worked up)* Angry! No, Furious! Incensed! We're not having that kind of talk in our synagogue. He's not staying here. Not in our synagogue, not in our town. We'll have none of it, I tell you. Blasphemy! Who does he think he is!
Dave	Wind it up, Kate, it's getting a bit ugly.
Kate	Thank you, sir. Trevor.

(Kate and scribe exit.)

Trevor	And now for other news. First, that story from Samaria . . .
Dave	Hold that one, Trevor. Go straight over to Daley. Things are happening in Nazareth.

Trevor	Well, we'll have to leave that story for now, because our reporter, Daley Bulletin, has news of further developments in Nazareth. Daley, what news?
Daley	Trevor. I'm standing near a high cliff just outside the town of Nazareth.
Trevor	That would be where the townspeople dispose of their rubbish, Daley?
Daley	Or twice a day, in some cases.
Trevor	Daley, tell us what is happening.
Daley	*(As though watching the events happen somewhere a little away from him)*
	A remarkable scene is taking place. At this very moment, a huge crowd of angry citizens is forcing Jesus up the hill, right up to the edge of the cliff. They are shouting abuse at him, pushing, shoving – it looks as though they actually intend to throw him over the edge. They're completely out of control. Two burly men have got behind him now – and they're pushing him, closer and closer to the edge.
Trevor	Are they actually going to throw him over the edge, just like a bag of refuse?
Daley	Yes, I do believe they are. Any minute, now. But, wait! Suddenly, Jesus has turned. And – this is amazing. He's just looking at the crowd – such a look! And now they are all falling back, away from him. And he's just walking right through the crowd, silently, with dignity, with authority, his face a mixture of sadness and determination.
Trevor	Where does he seem to be going?
Daley	Jesus is turning his back on Nazareth and heading off, away from the town where he grew up. This is Daley Bulletin, for News at Five Past Six, in Nazareth, absolutely gob-smacked, returning you to the studio.
Trevor	Thank you, Daley.

Dave   Wind it up, Trevor-luv. We're out of time.

Trevor   Well, that's the top story for today. Jesus of Nazareth, claiming to be God's anointed one, rejected by his own people. As Jesus himself put it, a prophet is honoured everywhere except in his own town. So, that's all we have time for this evening on News at Five Past Six. Stay with us here on Channel Five and a Half, the channel that brings you good news as well as bad. This is Trevor Cheeseburger, saying . . .

Dave   Say good night, Trevor.

Trevor   Good night, Dave.

Dave   No, good night everyone!

The Entire Cast

          Good night!

HERE IS THE NEWS
4. Sad News and Amazing News

Bible Base
Luke 23.1-24.35; John 18.28-20.18.

Introduction
(See also the general introduction for *Here is the News.*)
This sketch is a TV news report of the death of the Lord Jesus. Because of the seriousness of the subject matter, it is not appropriate to incorporate the kind of silly humour which is sprinkled liberally in the other three sketches in this series. The format, however, does allow for the drama and emotions of the events to emerge. The report is supposed to be happening live on the Sunday evening following the crucifixion. Christ is by then risen from the dead, but the news of this is only just beginning to filter through.

Cast
Dave the Director
Trevor Cheeseburger
Kate Grady
Daley Bulletin
Julie-Darling
Simon of Cyrene
Mary Magdalene

(NB If following up this drama, as suggested in the introduction, by getting groups of children to produce their own newspaper accounts of the events, the disciple John, as a witness of the crucifixion and resurrection, could be brought in for a press conference.)

(The sketch should start in a similar way to the previous three, with Dave the Director entering and calling everyone into action. The TV team busy themselves getting the studio ready. The two Biblical characters, when they enter later to be interviewed, should wear traditional costume.)

Dave   Right, everyone, two minutes to go. Come on now, luvvies. In your places. Get this studio straight. Quick as poss. It looks like a rubbish tip. Trevor, do something about your bow tie, luv. Where's make-up? Julie-Darling! Anyone seen Julie?

(Julie-Darling comes running on, carrying a news report.)

Julie-Darling *(With great excitement)*
Dave, quick, look at this. I've just received it from our Jerusalem office.

Dave Not now, Julie-Darling. We've got a programme starting in one minute. One minute, everybody.

Julie-Darling You'd better look at it, Dave. It's a big story.

Dave *(Reading and looking shocked)*
Oh, no!
(Leaping into action)
Right. Listen, everyone, we've got some really heavy stuff come through from Jerusalem. Drop all the other items. Quick, Trevor, look at this report and see how you can handle it.
(He hands Trevor the report.)
Time is short. Do what you can, everyone. This is serious. We'll try to get hold of Kate for an on-the-spot report as soon as we can. Right. Countdown to kick-off. Here we go. Ten seconds, nine, eight, seven, six, five, four, three, two, one . . . Cue intro.

Julie-Darling And now here on Channel Five and a Half, it's Sunday evening and time once again for News at Five Past Six, presented by Trevor Cheeseburger.

Dave Cue music.

(Music)

Off you go, Trevor.

Trevor Good evening.
(Very serious)
Jesus of Nazareth, the well-known teacher and healer, is dead. We have just received reports that on Friday afternoon the man that many called the Messiah, and some called the Son of God, was put to death, by edict of Pontius Pilate. Jesus of

Nazareth was crucified, along with two common thieves, on a hill outside Jerusalem city.

Dave   Right, Trevor-luv, we've got Kate in Jerusalem.

Trevor   Kate Grady brings an on-the-spot report from Jerusalem for News at Five Past Six. Kate.

Kate   Amidst extraordinary confusion here on Friday, Jesus, the teacher from Nazareth, was eventually taken away and crucified on the hill known locally as the Place of the Skull.

Trevor   Kate, can you tell us, what was the charge against him?

Kate   I wish I could tell you. The Jewish leaders accused him of blasphemy, claiming that he called himself the Son of God, but Pilate, the Roman governor, insisted he could "find no fault in the man." Pilate apparently tried everything he could think of to appease the Jewish leaders and to find some way of securing the release of Jesus. But without success.

Trevor   Kate, is there not a tradition that the Roman governor can release one prisoner at the time of the Jewish Passover?

Kate   Yes, Trevor, that's right. But when he offered the crowd the chance to set free either Jesus or a murderer called Barabbas, they chanted for Barabbas. Then, when the crowd started chanting 'crucify him, crucify him' Pilate handed Jesus over to them, and they led him away. He carried his own cross along the road out of the city, until, falling under the weight of it, he stumbled, and they called a man from the crowd to carry the cross for him. The man called Simon is here with me now.

(Simon enters to be interviewed by Kate.)

Kate   Simon, tell us what happened.

Simon   Well, I'd only come up to the city from the country for the Feast. And I heard all this commotion, people shouting and screaming, and then all these

104

women, wailing and weeping. I went to have a look, and there he was, dragging this huge cross. Then, when he started to stumble, they came across to the crowd, and one of the soldiers said, "Here, you, man, you look strong and healthy, you go and take over for him." Then, I was out there, carrying the cross. My, it was a weight.

Kate   And did Jesus speak to you?

Simon   Not a word. But as I followed him along the track, carrying his cross, he turned and looked at me and in his eyes there was a look which seemed to say, "Not just today, Simon. Not just today."

Kate   So the three of them, Jesus and·the two thieves, they were nailed to their crosses and left to die on the hillside?

Simon   It was terrible, I tell you. The pain he suffered. He was innocent, you know. That man never did anything wrong, I can tell you that for sure. I couldn't stay to watch. You'd better talk to some of the women.

(Simon exits, clearly upset. Mary takes his place.)

Kate   One of the followers of Jesus, a woman called Mary from Magdala, is with me now. Mary, what happened next?

Mary   It was amazing! He was hanging there, dying, nailed to that awful cross, and they were all jeering at him and mocking him, and he actually cried out, "Father, forgive them, forgive them; they don't know what they are doing." He just went on and on loving, right up to the end.

Kate   You obviously loved him greatly . . .

Mary   Loved him! You bet. I've given up everything I had to follow him! And now he's given everything . . .

Kate   So, describe to us your feelings, Mary.

Mary   *(Excited and confident)*
Oh, it's OK. Now. You see, this morning . . .

Kate	No, Friday afternoon, at the crucifixion . . .
Mary	Oh, then. I was heart-broken. I cried and cried. We women that were there, we thought it was the end of the world. The end of everything we had lived for. *(Change of mood)* But it's alright now, you see, because . . .
Kate	Exactly what time did Jesus die then?
Mary	Let's see. It was about mid-day when the sky suddenly went pitch black, and that went on for about three hours, and then, well, it must have been three o'clock in the afternoon.
Kate	Did you hear his last words?
Mary	He just said, very quietly, "It is finished." As though, I don't know, as though, somehow, he'd . . . won? Do you know what I mean? It wasn't . . . defeat. And then he cried out, "Father, into your hands I commit my spirit." And then he died.
Kate	The end of everything you had lived for.
Mary	That's what we thought. Then. But . . .
Kate	Did you attend the burial?
Mary	I followed behind with the other women. Two of the men, Joseph and Nicodemus, took the body down from the cross and laid it in Joseph's own tomb in a garden, just over there. And then they sealed the tomb with this huge stone.
Kate	Thank you, Mary. You are very brave. It must be hard for you to talk about this.
Mary	Oh no, it's OK. You see, because . . .
Dave	OK, Kate, that'll do, luvvie. Cut back to studio.
Kate	*(To the camera)* So, that was the end of Jesus of Nazareth.
Mary	No, it wasn't . . .

Kate	The man who had promised so much to his faithful band of followers is now dead and buried, his body lying in a sealed grave in a garden here in Jerusalem. The end of the road for Jesus of Nazareth. This is Kate Grady, for News at Five Past Six, with sad news from Jerusalem, returning you to the studio.
Mary	Wait. Let me . . .
Dave	Carry on, Trevor.

(Kate and Mary exit.)

| Trevor | So, Jesus of Nazareth, the man who claimed to be bringing good news for the world, is dead. So, was it all just an empty dream? Who knows? But what we do know is that Jesus is now just a fond memory in the minds of his dejected and pitiful followers. This is Trevor Cheeseburger, and that is the news on this sad Sunday evening. Now, over at the Weather Centre, let's see . . . |

(Daley Bulletin rushes in and takes his place, ready to report.)

Dave	Hold it, Trev. Scrap the weather forecast. We've got something really big coming in from Emmaus. Go over to Daley. Quick, luv. This is real headline stuff.
Trevor	Well, it seems as though we have more news coming in at this very moment. Our reporter, Daley Bulletin, is at a small village called Emmaus, about seven miles from Jerusalem. Daley.
Daley	*(Very excited)* The news here is absolutely sensational, Trevor. If the reports I have just heard are confirmed, this could be just about the greatest story in the history of broadcasting . . .

(All freeze.)

Light of the World

Bible Base
Genesis 1.1-3; John 3.19-20; John 1.1-14; Isaiah 60.1-3; John 12.36; John 8.12; 1 John 1.5-7.

Introduction
This is a dramatic event designed as the start to a Christmas carol service. It is reproduced here in the form originally used, which assumes the participation of a choir in the service. It may be modified for other situations. The dramatic impact of this piece depends upon effective lighting. Total blackout is required near the beginning and a burst of bright lighting near the end. For this latter effect we used a combination of an overhead projector and a slide projector hidden behind the pulpit, balanced precariously on piles of books. The drama contrasts the light of God, as revealed in Jesus, with the darkness of evil.

Cast
One actor
Two voices off-stage (amplified) – one male, dark and sinister; the other female, bright and angelic
The choir, one member of which acts as taper-bearer
Someone efficient to control the lights

(At the start of the service the choir assemble at the back of the church. At the end of the drama they will have processed to their places at the front.)

(The actor enters, takes position centre stage.)

Actor   In the beginning God created the heavens and the earth. And God said, let there be light, and there was . . .
(Pause)
. . . light.
(Looks around contentedly)
That's nice, isn't it!

(Suddenly all the lights go out – total blackout, if possible.)

Actor   Who did that? What's going on?

	(Walks about, stumbling noisily) I can't see a thing. Where are you? It's a bit scary. Is anybody there?
Voice 1	*(Off-stage, booming out of a loudspeaker – very sinister!)* Now that's better, isn't it! Yes, we prefer it like this. Nice and dark.
Actor	Who said that? Look, have you got any light over there, wherever you are? I can't see a thing. *(Knocks over something noisily)* Ouch!
Voice 1	*(Sinister laugh)* Ha, ha, ha, ha!
Actor	Wait a minute, I think I might have a match here, yes, here it is. *(Strikes match)* Ah, that's better, now I can see . . .
Voice 1	*(Angrily)* Put that light out!
Actor	*(Nervously)* Sorry. *(Blows out match.)*
Voice 1	That's better. I told you. We prefer it like this.
Voice 2	*(Off-stage, over a loudspeaker – confident and angelic)* People love darkness rather than light, because their deeds are evil. Everyone who does evil hates the light and will not come into the light for fear that their deeds will be exposed.

(One member of the choir switches on a torch and shines it around the roof.)

Actor	At last, some light. I say, would you be kind enough to shine that over here please? Hey, you with the light! Over here please . . .
Voice 1	*(Really angry!)*

I said, let there be darkness!

(Torch is switched off immediately.)

	And there was darkness. Lovely, cold, black, gloomy darkness.
Voice 2	See, darkness covers the face of the earth.
Actor	*(Sarcastically)* Yes, very true.
Voice 2	And thick darkness is over the peoples.
Actor	Oh, yes, very good, very observant. Is that the best you can do?
Voice 2	But the Lord rises upon you like the sun.
Actor	*(Excited)* What? Where?
Voice 2	And his glory appears over you.
Actor	Well, I'm blowed if I can see it!

(At this point one member of the choir lights a taper and begins to walk up the aisle to the front. Somewhere at the front there is a single candle, which the choir-member lights. The actor watches the lit taper pass by rather dubiously. All this happens during the following speech.)

Voice 2	The true light that gives light to every man was coming into the world. The Word became flesh and lived for a while among us. We have seen his glory, the glory of the one and only Son who came from the Father, full of grace and truth. *(Pause)* Light has come into the world!
Actor	*(Looking at the lit candle, with incredulity)* What, that?
Voice 1	*(Rather a bored tone of voice)* Excuse me, but would you mind putting out that light?
Actor	OK

	(Blows in the direction of the candle, but does not blow it out.)
Voice 1	*(Angry)* I said, out! *(Actor blows more furiously.)*
Voice 1	Out, out , OUT!
Voice 2	The light shines in the darkness, but the darkness . . .
Voice 1	I said, OUT!
Voice 2	. . . but the darkness has not overcome it!
Voice 1	*(Shouting frenetically)* O . . . ! U . . . ! T . . . ! OUT!
Actor	*(Giggling)* It won't go out!
Voice 1	*(Gradually fading away)* Out, out, out, please, someone, put it out . . .

(A flute or other solo instrument now starts to play quietly the melody of the opening carol. This continues and should be synchronised so that a suitable ending point is reached at the end of the drama.)

Voice 2	*(Triumphant)* Arise, shine, for your light has come! The glory of the Lord rises upon you!

(The front of the church is suddenly lit up with a burst of brilliant light. Actor gasps and falls on knees in worship. The choir then begin to walk up the aisles from the back of the church.)

	Nations will come to your light, and kings to the brightness of your dawn. Put your trust in the light while you have it, so that you may become children of light.

(The choir, when they reach the front of the church, form a group behind the actor, who then stands and faces the congregation.)

Actor & Choir	If we walk in the light as he is in the light, we have fellowship with one another.

Actor	And the blood of Jesus, his Son, purifies us from every sin.
Voice 2	Jesus said, I am the light of the world. Whoever follows me will never walk in darkness, but will have the light of life.
Actor	And God said, let there be light. And there was . . .

(Pause)

Jesus!

(As the word 'Jesus' is pronounced all the house lights come on. Exit the actor. The flute gets to an appropriate stopping point. The choir then go straight into singing the opening carol.)

The Nativity Scene

Bible Base
Matthew 6.33; John 14.15; John 7.46; Matthew 7.29; John 14.6;
Luke 22.54 and 63; John 19.16-18; Luke 23.44 and 46; Philippians
2.5-11.

Introduction
This is a sketch for a Christmas service. It is intended to remind
the audience that Jesus is not just a baby in a manger in a
Christmas card scene.

Cast
Mary
Joseph (non-speaking)
Elsie
Mabel
John

*(There is blackout. When the lights come up there is on the stage a
typical nativity scene, looking like a Christmas card, with a stable,
manger, Mary and Joseph posing appropriately. They remain static
throughout until just before the end of the sketch.)*

*(Elsie and Mabel, two caricatures of gossiping shoppers, enter with
full shopping baskets. Lots of 'oohs' and 'aahs' intersperse their
speech. Mabel has a habit of saying the last word or two of Elsie's
sentences with her – this is indicated by an asterisk (*) in the text.
John enters behind them and takes up a position in one corner of the
stage, with his back towards them – he is reading.)*

Mabel	They're only forty-six pence a pound in Tesco's, Elsie.
Elsie	I shall still get mine in Sainsbury's, Mabel. Always have done and always will. You can't change a habit of (*) a lifetime.
Mabel	*(Seeing the nativity scene)* Oh look, Else, it's one of them maternity scenes. You know, like on the Christmas cards.
Elsie	Nativity scenes, Mabel.

Mabel	Oh, yeah. But look, Else, innit nice. Look, can you see the mother Mary? Don't she look contentified.
Elsie	Yes. Don't she look (*) loverly.
Elsie & Mabel	*(Together)* Oh, yes.
Mabel	And look at Joseph. Just standing there. So dignitified.
Elsie	Yes. *(Pause)* Actually, he looks a bit fed up to me.
Mabel	Well, 'e don't get much of a look in, does 'e?
Elsie	No, suppose not. It must be a bit tedious all that answering the door and saying, 'Mother and baby doing well!' every time a shepherd or a wise man calls.

(They laugh.)

Mabel	But 'e looks nice though, don't 'e, that Joseph?
Elsie	Oh, yeah, he looks ever so (*) nice.
Mabel	I like that bit.
Elsie	What?
Mabel	You know, that bit where the shepherds and the wise men come to worship the Infant King . . .
Elsie	Oh, yeah. It's nice that bit. I wonder if we've missed it?
Mabel	Dunno. Let's wait and see.

(They are silent for a while, studying the scene intently.)

Elsie	Oh, just look at the little baby Jesus, Mabel. Don't he look a picture lying there in that (*) manger. *(Leaning forward, making 'baby noises')* Ooochie, goochie, goochie . . .
Mabel	Shh. Quiet, Else, you'll disturb 'im.
Elsie	*(All dewy-eyed and soppy)* It's just like the Christmas carol, isn't it? Away in a manger no crib (*) for a bed. The little Lord Jesus

lays down his (*) sweet head. The stars in the bright sky look down where (*) he lay. The little Lord Jesus asleep (*) in the hay. Aah!

Mabel   It takes you back though, don't it, all this Christmas stuff?

Elsie   How'd you mean, Mabel?

Mabel   You know, to when we were children. Do you remember Christmases when we were children?

Elsie   Yeah, we used to love it. But then Christmas really is for (*) the children.

Elsie & Mabel *(Together)*
Oh, yes.

Mabel   Oh, just look at his little hands, and his little dumpy arms.

Elsie   Oh, yes, isn't he (*) sweet.

John   *(Suddenly turning towards them)*
Excuse me, but who are you talking about?

Mabel   The little baby Jesus, look . . .

Elsie   Just like in the Christmas cards.

John   I see.
(Thoughtfully)
Jesus . . . wasn't he the man that said 'Seek first the kingdom of God and his righteousness'?

Elsie   I dunno. He's just a little baby lying in (*) a manger.

Mabel   Oh, look, Else, 'e's opening 'is little eyes!

Elsie   Aaah, don't you just love him?

John   Jesus . . . wasn't he the man who said 'If you love me, you will obey what I command'?

Mabel   *(Ignoring him)*
Don't you think it's very pictureskew all this stuff in the stable, with the straw and everything?

Elsie   Oh, yeah. And the star shining through the window, like shedding its heavenly light on the little baby's (*) face.

Elsie & Mabel	*(Together)*
	Oh, yes.
Mabel	Do you remember them maternity plays?
Elsie	Nativity plays, Mabel.
Mabel	Oh, yes.
Elsie & Mabel	*(Together, pointing to the sky and giggling like children)*
	'Behold we have seen his star in the East and have come to worship him!'
Elsie	Oh, weren't they loverly!
John	*(Excitedly turning the pages of his book, and reading)*
	That's right, Jesus of Nazareth. Didn't they say of him, 'No-one ever spoke the way this man does', were they not amazed at his teaching because he taught as one who had authority', and did not he himself say, 'All authority in heaven and earth has been given to me'? And didn't he even claim that he was 'the way, the truth and the life', yes, and say that 'no-one comes to God the Father except through him'?
Mabel	What's he going on about?
Elsie	I dunno. I think he's got religion or something.
Mabel	Oh, look, Else, did you notice the animals in the stable?
Elsie	Oh, yeah. Look, sheep, cows, donkeys.
Mabel	Look at the way they're looking at the baby.
Elsie	I think they know, don't you, you know, that he's someone (*) special.
Elsie & Mabel	*(Together)*
	Oh, yes.
John	*(Reading thoughtfully)*
	'Then seizing Jesus they led him away . . . The men who were guarding Jesus began mocking and beating him . . . Finally, Pilate handed him over to

them to be crucified . . . So the soldiers took charge of Jesus . . . Carrying his own cross he went out to the Place of the Skull . . . Here they crucified him. Darkness came over the whole land . . . Jesus cried out with a loud voice, Father, into your hands I commit my spirit. When he had said this he breathed his last.'

Elsie   Oh, do be quiet, will you.

Mabel   You'll upset the baby.

Elsie   I don't know. Some people got no idea what Christmas is all about.

(As John reads the following passage Mary and Joseph come to life. They attend to the baby. Joseph picks up the baby, hands him to Mary and they start to walk off as John gets to the end of his reading.)

John   'Christ Jesus, who being in very nature God, did not consider equality with God something to be grasped, but made himself nothing, taking the very nature of a servant, being made in human likeness. And being found in appearance as a man, he humbled himself, and became obedient to death. Even death on a cross! Therefore God exalted him to the highest place, and gave him the name that is above every name, that at the name of Jesus every knee should bow, in heaven and on earth and under the earth, and every tongue confess that Jesus Christ is Lord, to the . . . '

Mabel   *(Calling after Joseph and Mary)*
Oh, don't take the baby Jesus away!

Elsie   No, put him back in the manger.

Mary   *(Turns and looks at them both, and speaks very deliberately)*
Look, don't you understand – Jesus can't stay in the manger for ever.

(Blackout)

Guardian Angels

Bible Base
The Christmas story – Luke 2.1-20, Matthew 2.1-18. Also Micah 5.2; Jeremiah 31.15; Hosea 11.1; Isaiah 9.1-2; Psalm 41.9; Psalm 27.12; Isaiah 50.6; Isaiah 53.1-7 and 12; Psalm 22.7 and 16; Zachariah 12.10.

Introduction
The familiarity of the Christmas story is such that we sometimes lose our sense of how amazing it all is. This sketch tries to capture some of the sense of wonder that we should have that God should actually come into this world in the person of his Son in the way that he did that first Christmas.

Cast
Celesta, a junior angel
Philos, a senior angel
Harmon, leader of the angelic choir
(These parts may be played by actors of either sex.)

(Celesta, a junior angel, is standing near a table, looking down through binoculars [or a telescope], as though keeping watch on events on earth. On the table is a large old book [e.g. a pulpit Bible], and a copy of The Times. *After a while Celesta puts down the binoculars, sits down, picks up* The Times *and starts browsing through it. Philos enters, carrying some papers.)*

Philos   *(To someone outside)*
Right, sir, leave that with me. I must get back to my post now. I've left one of the junior angels on lookout.
(To Celesta)
Ah, Celesta, everything going OK down there?

Celesta   *(Guiltily putting down the newspaper, resuming lookout post and picking up binoculars)*
Oh, yes, everything's fine. It all seems to be going according to plan.

Philos	*(Sitting down, picking up newspaper and examining it suspiciously)* I see you've been reading *The Times* while on duty again. And I thought you were supposed to be a *guardian* angel!
Celesta	Sorry, boss.
Philos	Never mind. Now tell me, how far have they got?
Celesta	*(Peering through binoculars)* They've just reached the outskirts of Jerusalem. Just as well, they look as though they could do with a rest. It's been a tough journey, especially for the girl. She'll be looking forward to putting her feet up when they get to the city.
Philos	Oh, didn't you know? They're not staying in the city. They're going on to Bethlehem. That's the place that's been chosen.
Celesta	Bethlehem? You must be joking! Surely it's going to happen in Jerusalem! It would have to be somewhere special like that – not a dump like Bethlehem.

(Harmon enters, singing quietly and conducting an imaginary choir.)

Celesta	Harmon, have you heard this? Philos says that it's going to happen in Bethlehem of all places! Tell me it's a joke.
Harmon	*(Taking a seat at the table, and turning over pages of the Bible)* Well, well, you junior angels – don't they teach you anything in school these days? Listen to what is written in the great book: 'But you, Bethlehem, though you are small among the clans of Judah, out of you will come for me one who will be ruler over Israel . . . '
Celesta	Wow, Bethlehem! *(Moves to look through binoculars to a new position.)* Who would have thought it! He's full of surprises, isn't he! Now I wonder where in Bethlehem it will be

(Scanning the town)
– ah I've got it, the Royal Hotel! That must be it! Five-star luxury, hot and cold in all bedrooms, à la carte menu, fit for a king! It looks a bit crowded down there, though . . .

Philos   It will not be the Royal Hotel, Celesta. They won't have room for them there. They won't have room for them anywhere.
(Gets up and goes across to Celesta)
Look round the back of the hotel. Can you see a sort of rough shed where they keep the cattle?

Celesta   Yes . . .

Philos   Well - you're not going to like this - but, apparently, that is it. That is the chosen place!

Celesta   What! In there! Look, this is getting ridiculous. That's no place for a king to be born! Surely there must be room somewhere else for them to go!

Harmon   You really don't understand, do you? Do you not remember what is written?
(Reads)
'He grew up . . . like a root out of dry ground. He had . . . nothing in his appearance that we should desire him. He was despised and rejected by men.'

Philos   That is how it will be for him, in birth as in death, despised and rejected.

Celesta   I wish you two would stop talking in riddles. I'll never understand what's going on.

(Celesta resumes lookout position; Philos sits down and looks at papers; Harmon reads the book.)

Celesta   What's for tea today?

Philos   Angel Delight, again.

Celesta   Oh, that's . . . great! And how's the choir coming on, Harmon? All ready to announce the good news?

Harmon   Nearly ready.

120

Celesta	Who's the audience going to be? You know, for this 'hark, the herald angels sing' bit? Let me guess – all the top people will have to be there, I suppose, politicians, generals, chief priests, businessmen, captains of industry . . .
Philos	Look out to the west of the town, up on the hillside – there, what can you see?
Celesta	*(Looking through binoculars)* Sheep?
Philos	Yes . . . and what else?
Celesta	*(Scanning)* More sheep . . . sheep, sheep . . . ah, and some shepherds!
Philos	That's it. The shepherds.
Celesta	What about the shepherds?
Philos	That's who's been chosen for the first announcement of the birth. In exactly . . . *(Checks watch)* 48 hours, 32 minutes and 20 seconds from now, the full choir of heavenly angels, with full performing costume and specially designed lighting effects, will appear to that group of shepherds out there on the hillside and announce the birth of the promised Messiah!
Celesta	Wow! This gets crazier and crazier.
Harmon	We *have* got some of the intelligentsia lined up for the second bulletin. *(Standing and pointing)* Look over to the East, focus on region 634 . . . down there in that palace . . . can you see three men? They're probably reading some old books - they seem to do that most of the time, at least when they're not star-gazing, that is.
Celesta	Got them. Now they look a bit more like it! Three wise men if ever I saw them. And pretty wealthy too, I should say.

Harmon	Well, they're in for a bit of a surprise next week! We're going to move one of the stars from galaxy alpha four thousand over into the western sky. *(Laughs)* That'll get them jumping up and down with excitement – and I think they'll know what it means! *(Resumes seat)*
Celesta	I get it. They'll follow the star to Bethlehem . . .
Harmon & Philos	Right . . .
Celesta	. . . they'll find the newborn king . . .
Harmon & Philos	Right . . .
Celesta	. . . they'll give him gifts . . .
Harmon & Philos	Right . . .
Celesta	. . . and they'll worship him . . .
Harmon & Philos	Right . . .
Celesta	And then they'll take the good news to Jerusalem, where everyone will listen to them, because they're rich and clever, King Herod will be overjoyed and invite the new king and the family to the palace, where he will grow up, and everyone will love him and follow him, and the world will gradually all turn back to . . .
Harmon & Philos	Wrong!
Harmon	No, in fact, we shall have to warn the wise men not to tell Herod where the child is.
Philos	Herod will be so furious when he hears of the birth of a new king that he will order all the male children under two years of age to be put to death.
Celesta	What! He can't get away with that! *(Focuses binoculars on Herod)*

	Where is the swine . . . shall I zap him now?
Harmon	Calm down, Celesta, you must trust that it is all under control. It is all foretold in the great book. *(Finds place in the book and then reads)* 'A voice is heard in Ramah, mourning and weeping, Rachel weeping for her children and refusing to be comforted, because her children are no more.'
Philos	One of us will have to go down and warn the family to escape to Egypt.
Harmon	*(Reads)* 'Out of Egypt I called my Son' – you see, Celesta, it is all in the plan.
Celesta	*(Rather sourly)* I'm not sure I like this 'plan'. All these thousands of years of waiting, choirs of heavenly angels singing 'glory to God', moving stars around the universe, the miracle of the Son of God being conceived in a virgin, all these messages we've been taking down about the coming Messiah, all those promises about 'the people who walked in darkness seeing a great light'. And what have we had so far? The poor parents have had to trudge for days from their home in Nazareth, to finish up having their baby in a second-rate town, in what looks to me very much like a stable, fit only for animals, the news is going to be announced to a group of scruffy, ignorant shepherds, hundreds of innocent children are going to be massacred, and our chosen family is going to end up as refugees in, of all places, Egypt! Aren't there any good bits in the plan?
Philos	Oh, yes, there are good bits. When he begins his ministry the ordinary people will flock to hear his teaching, and his disciples will be amazed at the miracles, and at one point we'll even have crowds lining the route into Jerusalem, waving palm leaves, and shouting 'Hosanna to the Son of David', but none of that will solve the problem.
Celesta	Problem? What do you mean?

Harmon	Take a good close look at some of the people down there . . . go on, focus in on their hearts, their minds, their motives, their actions . . . what do you see?
Celesta	*(Moving binoculars around the audience)* I never realised it was that bad . . . oh, look at it! Pride, selfishness, greed, envy, anger, hatred, cruelty, materialism . . . it's horrible! Shall we zap the lot of them?
Harmon	You still don't understand, do you? The whole point is that he loves them!
Celesta	Loves them! What, that lot?
Philos	And that is why he's going to be born down there . . .
Celesta	I see, to live a good life . . .

Harmon & Philos
>   Right . . .

Celesta	And then they'll all see sense and get rid of all that evil in their hearts . . .

Harmon & Philos
>   Wrong!

Philos	No, I'm afraid it won't work like that. Look, let me show you how it will be done. We've just received these details of the final stages of the plan. *(Hands Celesta some papers)*
Celesta	*(Examines the papers, and becomes more and more horrified)* No . . . no, not that . . . no, it can't be . . . there must be some other way? *(Hands back papers)*
Philos	That is the plan.
Harmon	It is as written in the great book . . .
Celesta	*(Angry)* No, no! There must be some other way!
Harmon	*(Reading from the book)* 'Even my close friend, whom I trusted . . . has lifted his heel against me . . . '

Philos	*(Gets up and reads over Harmon's shoulder)* ' . . . false witnesses rise up against me, breathing out violence . . . '
Harmon	' . . . oppressed and . . . afflicted, . . . led like a lamb to the slaughter . . . '
Philos	' . . . mocking and spitting . . . '
Harmon	'He poured out his life unto death, and was numbered with the transgressors . . . '
Philos	' . . . they have pierced my hands and my feet . . . '
Harmon	'All who see me mock me, they hurl insults, . . . '
Philos	'They will look on me, the one they have pierced, and mourn for him as they mourn for an only child . . . '
Celesta	*(Having got more and more distressed during these readings)* No, stop it, there must be some other way, it's not fair! They can't do that. Not to him!
Philos	But it is because he loves them that he must go this way.
Harmon	*(Reads)* 'He was pierced for our transgressions.'

(Celesta moves towards the exit, looking back, and muttering 'There must be some other way', as the readings continue.)

Philos	'By his wounds we are healed . . . '
Harmon	'We all, like sheep, have gone astray, each of us has turned to his own way . . . '
Celesta	*(Shouts and exits)* I'm sorry, but I'll have to tell him that I'm not going to be party to this plan. There must be some other way!
Harmon	' . . . and the Lord has laid on him the iniquity of us all.' *(Pause)*

Philos I don't suppose there could be another way, could there? Does he really have to suffer like that . . . for them?

Harmon I don't know. I'm sure if there had been he would have taken it.

Philos He really must love them . . .

(Celesta re-enters, quietly picks up binoculars and carries on surveillance. The others look at Celesta in expectation. After a while Celesta speaks.)

Celesta *(Very serious)*
There is no other way.
(Pause, and then excitedly)
But you wait until you hear the next bit! This'll knock you out! There's going to be this tomb, right, and this huge boulder over the entrance, right, and one of us,
(Looking rather smug)
. . . well, me actually, has got to go down on the third day, and, pow! Over goes the boulder and then . . .
(Gets up and goes to stand between Philos and Harmon.)
Look, let me show you, it's all written here in the great book . . .
(Turns over pages excitedly)

(Blackout)

A Window in the Diary

Bible Base
Philippians 2.5-11.

Introduction
This sketch is unashamed satire. It is a gentle dig at the kind of person who drops in and out of church at Christmas and remains completely untouched by the significance of the events on which Christians focus at this time of year.

Cast
Henry and Freda Buckingham

(The Buckinghams are snobs. Freda is modelled on the Margot character in the TV series The Good Life. *Henry is probably a successful accountant in the City. The sketch revolves around a telephone conversation with the vicar of the local parish church, and takes place just before Christmas. The scene is the drawing-room of their neo-Georgian detached house. The sketch requires appropriate chairs for the two actors and a small table with a telephone.)*

Actor 1	*(Henry, but not yet in character)* Ladies and gentlemen
Actor 2	*(Freda, but not yet in character)* We present . . .
Actor 1	A Window in the Diary,
Actor 2	A short play . . .
Actor 1	That could not possibly be about anyone here this evening. *(Pause – then to Actor 2)* It couldn't be, could it?

(They look at audience, think about it, then dismiss the possibility.)

Together   No, of course not. Couldn't be.

(They go into character and take seats on opposite sides of a table, on which sits a telephone. Henry studies his diary, Freda reads some appropriate magazine, such as Vogue.*)*

Henry	We seem to have a window in the diary on Christmas morning, Freda. Thought I'd book us in for a service.
Freda	Service, darling? Will that be the Range Rover or the BMW?
Henry	No, you custard-brain. A service at the church. You know, worship the new-born King and all that. Look, I'll just give the vicar a bell and run through one or two details with him. *(Uses telephone)*
Freda	Good idea, Henry. We don't want a repeat of last year's fiasco.
Henry	Quite. Oh, hello, reverend. Henry Buckingham speaking . . . Buckingham, as in Palace. You know, neo-Georgian detached, corner opposite the church, double garage . . . yes, that's the one , . . . yes, Range Rover and BMW. Well, look, reverend, the thing is, the lady wife and I seem to have a bit of a window in the diary for Christmas morning. Thought we'd book in for a service . . . *(Mock laughter)* yes, very satirical, vicar.
Freda	What did he say, Henry?
Henry	He said, will that be the Range Rover or the BMW?
Freda	Find out what time the service is.
Henry	Right. Now, vicar, Christmas morning service. What parameters have you got pencilled in time-scale wise? . . . mm? . . . Eleven o'clock? *(To Freda)* Eleven o'clock kick-off, alright dear? *(To vicar)* Yes, we think we can run with that, reverend. The lady wife should have extracted the tangerine from the toe of the stocking by then. And, well, as I always say, Christmas wouldn't be Christmas without going to church . . . well, I suppose you would say that, wouldn't you?

Freda	Ask him about the carols, Henry.
Henry	Ah yes, the carols. Now, vicar, can you just assure us that we will be singing the good old traditional carols? . . . you know, Hark the herald.
Freda	Once in Royal David's thingy.
Henry	O come all ye faithful.
Freda	Away in a thingy.
Henry	Nothing by that modern chappie, please. What's his name, Freda?
Freda	Um, thingy Hendrix. Jimmy. No, Graham something. Graham . . .
Henry	Graham Snedrick. That's it. Now, vicar, you must realise that people don't put themselves out to come to church on Christmas day to sing *Shine, Jesus, Shine*. With drums. It's just that, well, frankly, vicar, last year the lady wife and I found the behaviour of your congregation in one or two places just a micro-dot embarrassing. I mean, I'm all for enthusiasm. In its place. Twickers on a Saturday afternoon, vicar, but not in church, not on Christmas morning.
Freda	Ask him about the lessons, Henry.
Henry	Ah yes, the lessons. Now, vicar, the lady wife and I would find it a little more agreeable if you could stick to reading from the proper Bible . . . well, for example, you must admit that 'the days were accomplished that she should be delivered' is just a touch more poetic than 'the time came for her to have her baby'.
Freda	And considerably less vulgar, if you ask me.
Henry	People turning out to fill your pews on a Christmas morning really do expect to hear the traditional readings, you know, from the original version . . . do I detect a touch of sarcasm there, vicar?
Freda	What did he say, Henry?
Henry	Would we prefer it if they read it in Greek?

Freda   Here, let me speak to him.
               (Takes phone)

Freda   Oh, hello, reverend. Freda Buckingham speaking . . .
               Buckingham, as in Palace . . . yes, every year, regular
               as clock-thingy. As Henry always says, Christmas
               wouldn't be Christmas without going to church . . .
               well, I suppose you would say that, wouldn't you . . .
               what? Every Sunday? All through the year? . . . What
               a quaint idea. Now, vicar, a word in your ear about
               your policy for selecting readers. People don't put on
               their best frocks and thingies to come to church to
               hear the lesson read by a bearded tramp in scruffy
               jeans and sandals, you know . . . oh, is he? Really?
               Well, it's no wonder state education is in such a mess.
               No, I think your flock would find it a little more
               felicitous if you went for someone a smidgen more
               refined, less like a refugee from Oxfam. Someone
               with, shall we say, a more cultured delivery . . . What
               me? Oh, vicar, fancy you thinking of asking me! Well,
               I suppose I could, if you twist my thingy . . . Have we
               got a Bible? Why, don't you have one at the church? . . .
               Oh, I see! Yes, I'm sure we've got one somewhere.
               (To Henry)
               Henry can you find that Gideon thingy you picked up
               in that hotel in Brighton?

(Henry gets up and looks for it)

               It's a brown one, over there, somewhere near the
               Liberty's catalogue.

Henry   *(While looking for Bible)*
               Have a word about the sermon, Freda, old girl.

Freda   Oh yes, the dreaded sermon.
               (Reprimanding)
               Eighteen and a half minutes last year, vicar . . . yes
               it was. I was looking at my watch all the time. Word
               of advice, vicar. Christmas is a very busy time. An
               eighteen and a half minutes lecture when people are
               anxious to get at the sherry and nibbles, well, it is a
               trifle self-indulgent.

Henry	Ah! Bible located. *(Brings Bible over and hands it to Freda.)*
Freda	One Bible and Parker roller-ball at the ready. Fire away . . . got it. Philippians chapter two, verses five to twelve. Check. Here, Henry, you talk to him, while I find it. *(Freda hands over phone and continues searching during the next speech.)*
Henry	Right. Now, vicar, about last year's sermon. All that stuff about God becoming man . . . 'the most significant event in the history of the world' . . . your very words, vicar, I assure you . . . Just a bit over the top, don't you think? I mean, baby born in stable, shepherds and angels and all that stuff about wise men and stars – it's a very nice story, vicar, but it hardly compares in significance with the invention of the internal combustion engine.
Freda	Or Harrods' Sale.
Henry	. . . he says have you found the reading yet, Freda?
Freda	No, still looking. Oh, look, there it is. Philippians. Oh, what a sweet little book.
Henry	The vicar here says that if you read that passage you'll find out what is so amazing about the Christmas story.
Freda	Good idea. Bit of prac' for Christmas day.
Henry	He says this is what was really going on when the Son of God was born in Bethlehem.
Freda	*(Reads – to start with she is just concerned about how beautiful her delivery is, but gradually she becomes interested in what she is reading . . .)* 'Your attitude should be the same as that of Christ Jesus, who, being in very nature God, did not consider equality with God something to be held on to, but made himself nothing, taking the very nature of a servant, being made in human likeness . . . '

Henry	Bit complex that, vicar . . . oh, I see . . . right . . . get the gist. Bit like the lady wife and I sending number one son to live in a flat on a council estate. Must be a good reason though. Not done lightly that sort of thing . . . what? To save people from their sins? *(To Freda)* He says read on a bit.
Freda	'And being found in appearance as a man, he humbled himself and became obedient to death – even death on a cross.'
Henry	That's what it's all about? No, I think you've got the wrong reading there, vicar. Sounds more like Easter to me.
Freda	I'm not so keen on Easter. All those Easter bunnies and those nasty little chocolate cream eggs. Prefer Christmas any time.
Henry	Not for me to teach you your job, vicar, but, if I were you, I'd major on the peace-and-goodwill-to-all theme. That's the kind of thing that strikes a chord at Christmas. You know, a good hefty cheque in the offering for famine relief, and then enjoy your turkey with a clear conscience.
Freda	Or he could go for the no-room-at-the-inn aspect. Very touching that part of the story.
Henry	Yes, good idea from the lady wife there, vicar. No room for Jesus. Strong human interest story. And you can really put the boot in for the innkeeper. Well, look, I hope we've been a bit of a help. Must dash now. Tempus fugit. Perhaps when you've got the order of service sorted you could fax us a copy . . . right, see you on the big day. And, Merry Christmas, vicar.
Freda	*(Calling out)* And a happy new thingy!
Henry	Well, that all seems very satisfactory. *(Writing in diary)* 'December 25th. Eleven a.m. . . . '

(The telephone rings – Freda picks it up.)

Freda   Freda Buckingham speaking. Oh, Fiona-darling, hello!

Henry   *(Still writing in diary)*
'. . . parish church: worship new-born King.'

Freda   Oh, how kind. Henry, it's George and Fiona.

(Henry looks puzzled)

George and Fiona Windsor. You know, Windsor, as in Castle. Want to know if we can go over for drinky-poos. Christmas morning, eleven-ish?

(Henry assents and amends diary)

. . . yes, love to come. No we haven't got anything special planned.

(Blackout)

The Shepherd and the Psychiatrist

Bible Base
Luke 2.8-20; John 1.46; Matthew 1.21-2.13.

Introduction
The idea for this sketch, like many of my most bizarre ideas, came to me in the bath. I had been trying for some weeks to come up with an original slant on the familiar Christmas story that would work as a piece of drama. On the radio was one of Dr Anthony Clare's programmes, *In the Psychiatrist's Chair*. So, what would have happened, I wondered, if one of the shepherds had gone to see a psychiatrist? This sketch is how I imagine the conversation might have gone . . .

Cast
Doctor (a female psychiatrist)
Receptionist
Adam Sheepdip (a shepherd)

(The Doctor is seated at her desk, writing. There is a vacant chair the other side of the desk. The scripts can be attached to the desk, if there isn't time for the two actors to learn their lines. There is a 'joke' built into the script which assumes this to be the case. Adam Sheepdip should be dressed in traditional Biblical shepherd costume. He should carry a crook in one hand and a sheep or lamb in the other – a stuffed toy or model, of course! He is very obviously a shepherd!)

Receptionist	*(Knocking, opening door and calling out)* The next patient's here to see you, doctor. Are you ready for him?
Doctor	Yes, send him in.
Receptionist	Doctor's ready to see you now, sir. OK? In you go, sir.

(Adam enters and stands in front of the doctor.)

Doctor	Good morning. *(Looking up)* Name, please?

Adam	Adam Sheepdip, sir.
Doctor	It's Madam, Adam.
Adam	No, no. That's Mister Adam.
	(Very deliberately)
	Mister Adam Sheepdip.
Doctor	*(Writing)*
	Mister Adam Sheepdip. Right.
	(Looking up)
	And what is your occupation, Mr Sheepdip?

(There is a bit of a pause, while Adam looks back and forth between the audience and the doctor, to emphasise that it is really rather obvious what his occupation is!)

Adam	Nuclear physicist.
Doctor	*(Writing)*
	Shepherd.
	(Looking up)
	Right. Please take a seat, Mr Sheepdip.
Adam	*(Picking up the chair and starting to walk out)*
	Ah, thank you, sir.
Doctor	Come back here! Sit down, Mr Sheepdip.

(He does so, putting down his crook and the sheep.)

	Thank you. Now, what seems to be the trouble then? What brings you to see a psychiatrist?
Adam	The visions, doctor. I've been having the visions.
Doctor	I see. Visions. And where were you when you had these . . . visions?
Adam	Well, me and my mates, we were just, as it were, abiding in the fields.
Doctor	Keeping watch over your flocks?
Adam	By night. That's it. Then I had the visions. In the sky. A bright, shining, dazzling, wondrous light.
Doctor	Really. Hmm.
	(Making notes)
	Seeing lights in the sky at night.

	(Looking up)
	Well, it looks to me, Mr Sheepdip, as though you may be suffering from what we in the profession call the nocturnal-cosmic-photo-phenomenological syndrome.
Adam	Oh. It looked to me more like the glory of God.
Doctor	So, how did you react to this light in the sky?
Adam	Well, we were sore afraid, weren't we?
Doctor	*(Writing)*
	Sore afraid.
	(To herself)
	Hmm. Evidence of anxiety-neurosis, a touch of paranoia . . .
Adam	*(Raising his head as he speaks, and pointing upwards)*
	Then I looked up straight into the light and, lo, I found myself staring at an angle.
Doctor	*(Imitating Adam's pose)*
	Staring at an angle? Yes, I suppose you would be.
Adam	*(Going out of character)*
	Well, that's what it says here.

(They look at the script together.)

Doctor	*(Whispering)*
	Angel.
Adam	Ooh! Sorry!
	(Clearing throat and going back into character)
	Staring at an angel!
Doctor	An angel. I see. You mean, a sort of heavenly being, with a shining appearance, floating around in space?
Adam	Something like that.
Doctor	*(Aside)*
	He's mad. Quite mad.
	(To Adam, humouring him)
	Wings?

136

Adam	Ah. You got me there, doctor. Couldn't see too clearly, you know. The light. It was so dazzling. But it was an angel alright. Because he spoke to us.
Doctor	He . . . spoke to you. I see. *(Writing and speaking to herself)* Audio-visual hallucinatory tendency. *(To Adam)* And what did he say, this angel?
Adam	He told us not to be afraid. So we weren't. So, you can cross out that bit about anxiety-neurosis. Thank you. And he said that he had good news for us. News of great joy. And not just for us, but for everyone. For the whole world.
Doctor	And what was this good news?
Adam	That a Saviour had been born. The Messiah. The one that God had promised. And he said we would find him, a baby wrapped in cloths and lying in a manger. In Bethlehem
Doctor	In a manger? What's that?
Adam	That's a long open box or trough in a stable, *et cetera*, for horses or cattle to eat from. That's from the French, *'manger'*, 'to eat'.
Doctor	Oh. I see. And this is where you would find the promised Messiah. Hmm. Seems a little unlikely. So, what happened next?
Adam	Well, suddenly, there was with the angel a multitude of the heavenly host.
Doctor	Speak English, please, Mr Sheepdip.
Adam	Sorry. Lots and lots of angels.
Doctor	What, like . . . filling the whole sky?
Adam	That's it. All around us. All singing about glory to God and peace on earth. Oh. It was mighty awe-inspiring.
Doctor	Hmm. *(Writing)*

Doctor	Pan-celestial-multi-faceted-audio-visual-halluci-natory tendency. *(Looking up)* Right. So, when the angels had gone, I suppose you trotted off to Bethlehem.
Adam	You bet we did. Well, we ran, rather than trotted. And we were thinking, if the baby's in a manger, it must be in some kind of cave or shed for animals.
Doctor	Ah, good thinking, Adam.
Adam	*(Excitedly)* So, we didn't go to any of the posh houses or hotels in Bethlehem. We hunted down all the back streets and alleys. The town was packed out, because of the census, you know. So many people! Well, anyway, eventually, we bumped into this man. And he tells us that there'd been a young couple, called Joseph and Mary, who'd come down from Nazareth for the census, and had knocked at their door looking for somewhere to stay, and the woman was obviously in labour, about to give birth. So they'd found room for them in the cow-shed round the back.
Doctor	So you went round to this cow-shed?
Adam	At once. And there they were: Mary and Joseph and the baby lying in a manger.
Doctor	*(Writing)* Mary and Joseph and the baby lying in a manger. Hmm. *(Looking up)* It was big, this manger, was it?
Adam	*(Pointing to doctor's notes)* No, that's: *(Very deliberately)* Mary and Joseph, comma, and the baby lying in a manger.
Doctor	Ah. And how did you find the mother and baby?

Adam	We just went in through the door and there they were.
Doctor	No, I mean, how were they both? After the birth. Doing well?
Adam	Oh, yes. They were in a stable condition.
Doctor	So, this baby. Supposed to be the Saviour of the world. In a feeding-trough. In a cow-shed.
Adam	Well, it seemed unlikely. Granted. I mean, a stinking old cow-shed, no better than the place that me and my mates kip down in at night. And a young, ordinary couple from Nazareth of all places.
Doctor	Ah, yes, the old saying: can anything good come out of Nazareth?
Adam	And the baby. Didn't seem anything special. Well, they all look the same, these new-born babies, don't thcy. But, doctor, I have never, in all my life, felt the presence of God like I felt it in that stable. It sent shivers through my old body. It was as though we had stepped into the Holy of Holies. As though we were present at a turning-point in the history of the world. And it was all happening there in a stable in Bethlehem. And we were the first to know about it. A bunch of scruffy old shepherds! And then this wonderful feeling of peace with God and real deep-down joy seemed to come all over me.
Doctor	Hmm. Very interesting. And what did thcy call tho baby?
Adam	(Reverently, looking upwards) Jesus. (Looking at doctor again) That means Saviour, you know. Because he will save us from our sins. Just like the angel said. "Today in Bethlehem a Saviour has been born." And then Mary, she tells us of another special name, a kind of secret name, that she only dares to speak in a whisper.

Doctor	*(Whispering)* What's that?
Adam	*(Whispering)* Immanuel.
Doctor	*(Still whispering)* And what does that mean? Immanuel.
Adam	*(Still whispering)* It means . . . God . . . with . . . us.
Doctor	Right, well, I think I've got all that. *(She makes notes and then continues.)* So, how can I help you, Mr Sheepdip?
Adam	Well, doctor. The thing is – it can't be true, can it? This baby, lying in a feeding-trough in a stable in Bethlehem, born of an ordinary young woman from Nazareth. This can't really be God. God come to be with us. God become a human being. Not like that. Surely, this can't be the way in which the Saviour of the world will come.
Doctor	Well, as you say, it does seem all rather unlikely.
Adam	But it happened, doctor. It all actually happened. The lights in the night sky, the angels, them telling us to go to Bethlehem, and us finding it all just like they said. And the thing is, doctor, if it's true, if this Jesus really is God coming into our world, then, well, nothing will ever be the same again, will it? I mean, if God comes to us like that, well, even an old shepherd like me has got a chance.
Doctor	Or even a sceptical old psychiatrist, like me?
Adam	Every one of us! It's as though God is saying, I'll step down into your world, so I can save you from your sins and bring you into my kingdom. What do you think, doctor? Can it all be true? Or am I just a stupid old shepherd, with a – what is it? *(Picking up the doctor's notes)* a "pan-celestial-multi-faceted-audio-visual-hallucinatory tendency", suffering from the "nocturnal-

140

cosmic-photo-phenomenological syndrome"? What shall I do about it all, doctor? What shall I do?

Doctor Well, Mr Sheepdip, speaking as a professional, my best advice to you, is . . . just try to forget all about it.

Adam *(Standing up, indignantly)*
Forget all about it?

Doctor Yes, just try to put it all out of your mind.

Adam Sorry, doctor, but there's no way I can forget about it. The events of that night. No, they'll live with me for the rest of my life. I can't just forget all about it.

Doctor Well, alright then. I tell you what. Just think about it, what shall we say, once a year? Yes, that's the way to deal with it. Once a year, allow yourself to remember the visions and the angels and the baby in the manger. And then for the rest of the year just forget all about it, put it all out of your mind and get on with your life.
(Leaning forward, seriously)
Mr Sheepdip. Your sheep need you.

(Picking up his crook and the sheep, Adam starts to leave, shaking his head, mumbling, confused.)

Adam Thank you, doctor. Yes, I suppose I'd better get back . . . to the sheep . . . yes . . . well . . . forget about it . . . right . . .

(He exits. The doctor sits, making notes. After a few seconds silence, Adam is heard shouting, very positively, off-stage . . .)

Adam Forget about it! Huh! Not likely!

(The Receptionist knocks on the door and steps in.)

Receptionist Your next patient is here, doctor.

Doctor Right. Send him in.

Receptionist It's some wise guy, going on about a star.

(Blackout)

Related titles published by National Society/Church House Publishing

Sketches from Scripture
Derek Haylock

Sketches to make you laugh . . . and to make you think, including *The Prodigal Daughter* (a new twist to the familiar story), *A Grave Buisness* (the story of the raising of Lazarus) and *The Least of These* (focusing on the needs of children worldwide).

You've Got It Wrong Again, Gabriel!
Alison Leonard

A full-length nativity play in two acts featuring Everyperson (an inquisitive little girl) who asks pertinent questions of Gabriel (a rather diffident archangel) about the meaning of the events in the Christmas story. The audience participates by singing carols at various points.

THE NATIONAL SOCIETY
A Christian Voice in Education

The National Society (Church of England) for Promoting Religious Education is a charity which supports all those involved in Christian education – teachers and school governors, students and parents, clergy and lay people – with the resources of its RE Centres, archives, courses and conferences.

Founded in 1811, the Society was chiefly responsible for setting up the nationwide network of Church schools in England and Wales and still provides grants for building projects and legal and administrative advice for headteachers and governors. It now publishes a wide range of books, pamphlets and audio-visual items, and two magazines *Crosscurrent* and *Together*.

For details of membership of the Society or to receive a copy of our current catalogue please contact:

> The Promotions Secretary,
> The National Society,
> Church House,
> Great Smith Street,
> London SW1P 3NZ
> Tel: 071-222 1672